poets

LESSONS IN LIFE

Edited by Steve Twelvetree

First published in Great Britain in 2002 by
YOUNG WRITERS
Remus House,
Coltsfoot Drive,
Peterborough, PE2 9JX
Telephone (01733) 890066

HB ISBN 0 75434 014 7
SB ISBN 0 75434 015 5

FOREWORD

As part of our ongoing pursuit to present a showcase of today's best up-and-coming authors, Young Writers is now proud to present its 'Teen Poets' series.

Few periods in life are more turbulent - or more crucial in human development than in the early teens. The struggles and trials faced daily can shape and mould our developing persona as we take a tentative step towards our early adult lives. The 'Teen Poets' series aims to bring these growing tribulations to light, providing a valuable snapshot into the thoughts and poetic visions of the teenage mind.

Lessons In Life offers a selection of these poems, as the young writers within tackle a range of vital issues whilst also sharing with us the lighter side of teenage life. The result is a valuable and stimulating insight into the mind-set of the modern youth, and a challenging read for many years to come.

CONTENTS

The Poems

MATTER TO MEMORIES

A boat we must sail, or an anchor to cast?
The last or the start, or the start of the last?

We prevent it and praise it,
We push and we pull,
But there is only one future,
Our efforts are null.

The darkening of minds,
The fading of light.
The end of a day,
And the start of a night.

The slow ringing bells,
Dull beat of drum,
Fog fills our hearts,
The light, gone.

Daylight is broken,
Moonlight can rise
Light is eternal,
Outliving our cries.

Light reignites,
Matter departs.
Light survives,
Warming hearts.

Never surrender,
Always live on.
As long as we live,
The light is not gone.

Though the light is eternal,
Light, we surrender.
In the world there's one constant,
We all meet . . . the end.

Oliver De-Vine (14)

My Room Is Such A Mess!

My room is like a pig-sty
My mother would like to know why,
There are clothes on the floor
And posters on the door,
I really should clean up more!

It's not very fair
That my CDs and tapes are everywhere,
My wardrobe's a tip,
I'll probably trip
And do a backflip!

My room is such a mess.
I wish there was a button to press,
To make it all clean,
Like an angel's just been,
And it's finally fit to be seen!

Anisha Daudia (13)

Sunrise

As the sun creeps up,
Like Earth's golden cup,
I see the colours swirl,
With beauty in every curl,
Deep red and orange mixed with gold,
Enchantment never sold.
In the warm summer dawn,
So wakes up the fawn,
While the cold winter rise,
So the dark freeze dies,
Unknown the secrets held,
From us strongly withheld.

Katie Derbyshire (14)

PAT

There once was a girl called Pat
who was very, very fat.
She got fatter and fatter
and eventually . . . splatter!
And that was the end of Pat.

The reason why Pat went splat
was simply because she was fat.
She ate her mum, dad and cat
and then she ate her friend's pet bat!
She ate her rat,
and then her hat
and then tripped over the neighbour's mat
and *splat!*
And that was the end of Pat.

If you ever get a little bit fat
just remember this story about Pat,
she went *splat!*
(You don't want to go *splat,* do you?)

Caroline Williams (15)

SADNESS

Sadness is a misty grey.
It tastes like tears dripping in your mouth
And smells like a damp cellar.
Sadness looks like a dead person's photo,
It sounds like a baby crying
And feels like tears running down your face.

Jeff Wyatt (13)

HOLDING ON

I can feel you hurting,
I can feel your pain,
Please don't lock me out,
We're going through the same.

I knew this wasn't meant to be,
I shouldn't have got involved.
Why did you have to make me feel so special?
Why did you have to make me feel so bad?

Can't you see I love you?
Can't you see I care?
I don't want to lose you,
You mean too much to me.

You broke down my defences,
You tore down all my walls.
Now you've left me stranded
And expect me not to hurt.

You have used me
And abused me.
You have scarred me
With your love.

It pains me to even think about you.
Your name pierces my heart.
I thought we had something different -
Something we could share.

I wanted us to last,
Longer than we have.
Were we ever intimate,
Or did I just imagine it?

Did you ever feel the same?
Is it really worth the pain?
I just wanted to hold you
Forever in my arms.

Georgie King (15)

IF I RULED THE WORLD

I   magine if I ruled the world
F   or I would be able to make peace among all people.

I   f I made no such word as pain, perhaps there'd be a lot less
    hurt and a lot more shame.
R   ace, does this play a big part in life or is it just the colour
    marked upon our face?
U   nited we stand as a group, as a nation,
L   et us live together, side by side, forever while in peace.
E   verybody hurts but for unnecessary reasons,
D   ay after day a hurtful event could have been prevented.

T   o some these mean nothing, it didn't affect them, why worry?
H   ate, such a strong word, do we use it in the right circumstances?
E   nd the wars, there's been enough bloodshed.

W   orld Trade Center, September 11th, didn't that make us realise?
O   ver the seas, near and far, these things all happen.
R   eady for a new world, do people realise we're in the 21st century?
L   et us get along in a life in which we belong.
D   o people agree when I say put an end to wars, put aside people's
    differences? Who cares if others are different? Certainly not me.

So . . . *Think* . . .
If I ruled the world.

Amy White (13)

FRIENDS!

My friends are the very best you could have,
I wouldn't change them for the world!
They each have qualities that I love and hate,
And ones that I admire.

First of all there is Stacey,
She loves to do my hair!
She talks all the time, but never in rhyme
And *always* thinks she's right!

Next in line is Lizzie,
The baby of the group!
She's good at maths, compared to me,
And can do the hula-hoop!

Thirdly there is Sarah,
To us she's called Li'l Red!
She loves wearing high heels and
Dropping her sister on her head!

Last, but not least, is Lorna!
She is blonde, but is not dumb.
She acts like Phoebe from Friends all the time,
When you're with her you're never glum!

I don't know what they think of me,
But hopefully it's not all bad!
I know we'll be friends forever,
And for this I am glad!

Louise Northey (15)

TEENAGE YEARS!

Mood swings,
Spotty phases;
Mothers nagging,
Writing pages!
Arguing loads,
Breaking up;
Hugging loads,
Making up!
Nothing's fair,
Everything hurts;
Your head is spinning,
In the dirt!
Rumours running,
Having dates;
Being broke,
Then just mates!
Fancying people,
Getting stressed;
Mad and mental,
People have guessed!
Chewing gum,
Smoking fags;
And other things,
That are bad!
Never tidy,
Never right;
Teenage years,
Are one hell of a fight!

Caley Robertson (13)

THE PARTY

Everyone said it was just a laugh,
You could join in if you wanted,
You didn't have to.
No, it wasn't like that!

Everyone was drinking,
Lucy's mum just sat there and let it happen.

If you didn't drink, they would force feed you the strongest
thing they could find,
Then you would be so drunk you would want more.

Things got nasty!

Everyone said it was just a laugh,
You could join in if you wanted,
You didn't have to.
No, it wasn't like that!

Everyone was drinking,
Lucy's mum just sat there and let it happen.

Katie Lockett (13)

THE SEASIDE

Sitting on the beach one day
Sun, sea and sand
'Look,' I said, 'here comes Mummy
With something in her hand.'
'Oh yes,' I say, 'yummy ice cream,'
Then I suddenly wake up
The whole thing's a
Dream.

Anna Harper (15)

TIME

Time to laugh,
Time to cry,
Time to live
Until we die.

Bullies win,
Outcasts lose,
Bullies forget,
Outcasts muse.

I am far
From Love's recluse,
So I suffer
Hate's abuse.

Fair are we?
When different is poor,
And social standing
Rules our lore.

Trapped am I,
By society's noose,
May independence
Set me loose.

Night and day
We fight a war,
Time we need
For wounds still sore.

Time to sing
A twilight rhyme,
Time to think,
Time for Time.

Mandy Lester (13)

MY FEELINGS BEFORE AND AFTER MENTORING

Before I had a mentor
My life was such a mess,
No one there to listen
No one who cared less.

I felt so low and empty
I knew I was alone,
No friends to go out with
No one cared at home.

My school life was a misery
My home life made me cry,
I felt so sad and ugly
I just wanted to die.

Then I met my mentor
And she listened when I spoke,
I started wanting to live
And was happy when I woke.

She told me I was beautiful,
She told me people cared,
She told me to be proud of me
And never to be scared.

She taught me how to love myself
And never be ashamed
She understands how I feel
And says I'm not to blame.

Now I have loads of mates
And school I love to go
Just having someone there who listens
Has helped so much I know.

To Marion I will always be grateful
And have thanks for being there
When no one else was.

Emma McGowan (15)

BENEATH THE ELM TREE

I feel the soft whispering breeze
Cooling my skin, replenishing my soul,
Reminding me that I'm not alone;
Wherever it goes, my mind shall follow.

I hear the rustling of the leaves
In the trees above my head,
Filling silence's impending gap,
Opening another, which fills with thought.

I see the glittering golden sun
Partially concealed beneath the horizon,
Igniting the sky in a fire of colour,
Illuminating my spirit in a light of emotion.

I smell the aroma of summer's flowers,
With every breath I am reminded
Of nature's presence, its beauty, its perfection,
That within my soul, this beauty is mirrored.

I know for certain these cogitations
Are as much mine as are my memories,
And although this moment will surely pass,
A part of me will remain right here
Forever.

Vanessa Jackson (15)

THE FEELINGS OF A TEENAGE GIRL

I am a teenager,
My name is Kim,
Sometimes I feel
Like I've been thrown in a bin.

Sometimes I'm happy,
Sometimes I'm sad,
Sometimes life is good,
Sometimes it's bad.

Sometimes I'm excited
When I go on a trip,
Sometimes I'm sad,
Like I've been thrown on a skip.

Sometimes it's great
When they're my mates,
Other times I want to cry,
When they say, 'Go and die.'

School is good,
But it can be bad,
When the other kids
Make you mad.

So I see Julie,
She's my mentor,
She cheers me up when I'm sad
And tells me that those kids are bad.

Kimberley Ward (14)

LIFE

Take the time to stop and think
Don't live your life so fast
Maybe you're forgetting
Things that happened in the past

Cherish everything you have
Don't know how long it'll last
Take the time to look around
Long life is very vast

Each day may be difficult
May find it very hard
But in the end it's worth it
Loved ones you should guard

Tell someone that you love them
Bring hope into their lives
Let them know how much you care
And help them to survive

Every day is a new day
Better than before
If you keep trying and work hard
You can only achieve more

Nothing's as bad as it seems
You just need to find the good part
Search for the truth and never give up
Happiness lies within your heart

Take the time to stop and think
Take the time to stay
Your mind may control you
But let your heart lead the way.

Leana King (14)

SPRING

Spring is a lovely time of year,
With blossom on trees, pink and white
Birds start to sing
And children come out to play.

Beautiful flowers and green leaves.

Little buds on trees open up again
Flowers start to grow
With little shoots showing
And grass starts to go a lush green.

Beautiful flowers and green leaves.

The weather gets warmer
And the sun glares down on us
The air starts to smell sweet
From daffodils and other flowers.

Beautiful flowers and green leaves.

Emma Hake (13)

NO-ONE UNDERSTANDS US

U   sually they blame our hormones, they would
N   ever think it might be something else, we are
D   ifferent to adults, they think now we've aged
E   leven and over we're grown up, they think we're
R   eady to join the adult world and we've grown up
S   ome of us are growing up, but not all of us are
T   hey've been through it, they know what it's like
A   nd they should understand us but they don't
N   ot even if you tell them what's wrong, they still
D   on't understand!

Alice Foster (14)

WAR

Why do we fight?
Violence is wrong,
Many will die,
The battle is long.

Why do we do it,
When we could be friends?
If we tried hard,
We could make amends.

The children who suffer the rages of war,
Grow up to remember,
They do not want more.

Peace in the world,
Is all I desire,
Peace should be natural,
Like wind, rain and fire.

Joanne Morrissey (13)

FANTASY FLIGHT

The dragon flew by, glittering in the night,
Shining on her scales was creamy moonlight.
Elegant as a swan, deadly as a snake,
All things gazed at her shimmering wake.
Starlight seemed to fade as she went by,
As did night-time sounds when she trumpeted her cry.
Her scales were iridescent, gold and silver,
Her glory was enough to make you shiver.
She flew straight on, up to the horizon,
Where she could see the sun was rising.
And still she flew, to meet the dawn,
Wanting to see where her new life would be born.

Lara Shepherd (14)

IN DREAMS

Dreams are full of colours,
there is no black or white,
there is no Heaven or Hell,
nor hunger, ignorance or spite.
In this world there is no darkness
it is covered with eternal light.
There is no hatred or war here
and children are not taught to fight.

In dreams the poor are rich
and the rich are humble too.
In dreams we have no grudges
it is never *me* and *you*.
This world is just one world
no third or second, as if in a queue.
Here there are no barriers,
doors are open; you can step right through.

In dreams there is unity
where no one is to blame
and those who once had nothing,
no longer live in shame.
And in dreams there is no war,
no suffering and no gain
and in dreams we are not different,
we can all see things the same.

However we are cursed,
to dream such a beautiful place,
because in our world
there is religion, war and race.
But wouldn't it be something
If one day our children's children could say,
'The dream which our ancestors had
we are living here today.'

Rachel Conboy (14)

TRUE COLOURS

There is a colour for everything I feel,
I am many colours,
All my colours are real.

I am blue; I am sad.
Maybe I feel guilty for something I've done bad.
My tears so blue wash my troubles away,
Everything that hurt me from the night or the day.

I am angry; I am red,
A volcano is going to erupt inside my head.
I am screaming, frowning,
I *hate* something.

I am envious; I am green,
There is something I want that I've seen.
Why can't I have that?
I am jealous: I want that!

I am happy: I am yellow,
In this colour I don't feel low.
I am laughing, having fun,
Time passes quickly the day is done.

I am transparent; I am clear,
If I have a feeling you will hear.
You can see my happiness, my grief, my pain,
You can read me like a book over and over again.

There is a colour for everything I feel,
Yellow is my favourite, it takes away the blue.
Red shouts at green, they hurt me and others,
With clearness you can see my pain.
And then there is white,
So pure, so bright,
She brings hope again.

Laura Platt (13)

THE PROBLEMS WITH TEENS!

Who said your teen years were the best years of your life?
Every day's the same; full of struggle and strife!
So many complications, so many things to do,
So much pressure is building up and causing anger too!

It seems like I can't do anything right,
Problems with your friends may cause you to fight!
School work, adolescence, arguments with Dad and Mum,
How many more problems are going to come?

No one seems to understand,
All I need is a helping hand.
It's nice to know you're not alone,
In these teen years that have grown.

Laina Fudgell (14)

WHY?

Why does the world have war
And why do some people ask for more?

Why do people marry and then divorce
And why are some people driven off course?

Why do people fall in love
And why is the sign for peace a white dove?

Why are animals kept in cages
And why don't animals live for ages?

Why do people cry
And why do people sigh?

Why do people always ask why
And why do people have to die?

Nikki Ryan (13)

WHEN DOES THE WORLD STOP TURNING?

When does the world stop turning?
When you say you love me?
When you say everything will be fine?
I don't think so
The world doesn't stop moving . . . for anybody
Nobody has the strength,
The will and determination
To make everything right
No amount of energy and love, pure as it may be
Can change life.
Well done for your efforts, but
You can't stop this life
You know it's out of reach
Just stop trying,
Just stop, don't move
The world won't stop turning for you.

Alice Barnes (14)

REFLECTIONS

Looking back at me,
A blank canvas of a face,
with wrinkles,
Her nose rounded and short,
Her double chin sagging,
Her pale lips,
Her eyes so sad,
so lonely,
I see this face every day
since her husband passed away
Last year on her birthday.

Nadia El-Sayed (13)

THE WORLD CUP 2002

The World Cup, what a terrific run,
with three lions on our shirts and hoping to go far.
To start we drew with the Greeks and qualified to start our
exciting journey ahead.
The World Cup Finals 2002 in Japan and Korea.
We drew with Sweden and thrashed the Argie Bargies too.
Within the group stages to certify qualification into the
important second round,
we drew with Nigeria who were sent home.
We beat the Danish 3-0 and made it to the quarters where
the Brazilians were too good by far.
So we were sent home, miserable but we had still made a
great achievement, so heads up and smile it's not so bad.
But the other annoying disappointment was Germany
were in the semis after beating USA,
let's just hope they go no further.
Europe beware you're in for a scare in Euro 2004.

Tara Brambor (14)

TRAPPED

I try to understand the way I am,
I try to find something pleasing about me,
But it's hard when you are trapped inside this kind of body.
It never used to get to me much before,
But now I'm a teenager it bothers me more and more.
I wish I could stop finding problems and faults
And hoping it will have disappeared by the time I'm an adult.
I feel trapped in this body,
I feel somehow it doesn't belong to me,
But I guess I should be thankful
That it doesn't match my personality.

Melanie Roe

WHERE DO I BELONG?

The sun rose over the Pamirs
Prayer calls drifted over the dusty land
Sheep graze on dry grass and shrubs
An occasional bird sang, this is Tajikistan

The women cook and go for water
Men and boys work in the fields
Children using rubbish as toys,
Life is too primitive for this foreign girl

I'm stared at for my foreign looks
I'm different, yet I'm accepted
In a way I'm one of them, but
It's hard to call a foreign place home

The sun rose but remained behind clouds
Bird calls drifted over green rolling hills
Green grass for a sheep to feast on
Rainy days and cold weather, this is England

The men and women go to work
While children spend their days at school
TV, dates, Internet, T-shirts,
Life is too modern for this dazed girl

I'm stared at for the things I say,
I'm different, can I be accepted?
Language the same, looks the same, but
I'm a stranger in my own world

Is there a place where I belong?
A place where I'm not pressured to fit in?
Just to be a mix, to be just me.
There is one now, but in my dreams.

Karissa M Taylor (13)

THAT SPECIAL BOY OF MINE

There he is again
That special boy of mine,
With his neatly combed hair
Wow, he looks so fine.
He's coming over,
My knees wobble like jelly,
He is so cute
I have butterflies in my belly.
What should I say?
How should I react?
For he is so cool
And that's a fact.
He winks one eye in my direction
With a grin on his face,
Has he guessed my affection?
Well one thing's for certain
I think I'm in love,
With this boy I'm sitting
On cloud nine up above.

Natasha Allen (14)

OUR FAMILY

Our family is everything to us,
We stick together all the time,
Through thick and thin,
As we are the finest of the fine.

We are number one,
And we will always be,
The best family ever,
At number twenty-three.

We have a lovely family tree,
With Grandfather at the start,
Going all the way down to my second cousins,
Who complete our family by doing their part.

So, here is a short poem,
About my caring, loving family,
Whichever way you see us,
Together we will always be.

Sadia Chaudry (13)

TEEN WORLD

After twelve you turn into a teen
And get to explore where you've never been,
Getting homework, pile after pile.
Just can't be seen without the latest mobile.
Now you want make-up not teddies or toys
And you're always thinking about boyfriends and boys,
Always putting on make-up and counting your spots
And brushing your hair to get out the knots,
You hang around in gangs at school.
Plus you always do your best to look cool.
Your hair gets more greasy and you start to sweat
And more soap and deodorant is what you need to get,
Your hormones go up and then they come down,
One minutes a smile and then it's a frown,
You like clothes expensive, you'll just never learn
And you think that your parents have money to burn,
You like to go clubbing and stay out real late,
Or go to the cinema with your latest hot date
And trouble may cross your path every day,
But your parents can't live without you, no way!

Amanda Baldwin (12)

BEING A TEEN . . .

Being a teen is really tough,
You have to deal with lots of weird stuff,
Spots and hairs are such a pain,
So is homework, it drives you insane.

Being a teen is also quite fun,
You get to go out and leave your sis at home,
You get to wear make-up and buy lots of clothes,
But you still get cross with the spot on your nose.

Being a teen is very strange,
You have to go through lots of change,
You go through mood swings and drive your mum mad,
Sometimes you can feel really sad.

Being a teen is quite cool,
Even though you embarrass yourself and end up a right fool,
You get to stay up all night and spend ages on the phone,
You like to be independent and left alone.

Being a teen can make your life hell,
But, we all know it can have is good points as well!

Alisha Oakey (13)

EYES

They follow me as I walk by
They do and I can feel them
Watching me, every step I take
I just want to get through one day without someone staring
Kids stare
Adults stare
Is there anyone who doesn't stare?
   No!

Kimberley Potts (14)

THE LONELY ONES

A smile so sweet is priceless,
it devours another person in happiness,
but did you ever look into
that person's eyes, and see how much their heart
really cries? The eyes
reflect a person's
soul. When sad,
eyes are just an endless
hole. Brave faces that
show not one feeling, so no one
can guess their mind is reeling.
The loneliness fills them deeply, all the
time they get more sleepy, until they drift
into uneasy dreams, with creepy
ghouls and ghastly fiends.
Hearts will break
and souls are sad.
We call them
the lonely
ones.

Nikki Walker (14)

DREAMS

I've got a lot of dreams
For my life
But they can only be
When I make them happen
Happiness lies
In my own hands
So only I
Can make my dreams come true.

Laura Smith (15)

GOODBYE DEAR CAT...

It's my fault,
everything just came to a halt,
as you lay there,
tranquillised and bare.
I thought of it as a joke,
when I gave you a poke.
I put you outside, in the cold,
but I knew it was time, for you were so old.
Goodbye dear cat...

The leaves sang in sadness,
for then things became madness,
as death neared you,
my heart gave a bellow,
but you laughed at the face of it,
although your life is ending in a pit.
Goodbye dear cat...

Leaves with golden rings around the stem,
then your eyes of which were gems,
shone like rays of the sun,
everything seemed to weigh a tonne.
Goodbye dear cat...

It's all my fault,
everything just came to a halt.

Jagdish Kaur (14)

MY ANGER

My anger is like a raging waterfall,
Water crashing on the rocks,
Splashing everywhere,
Making a deafening crashing noise,
Turning the rocks a pale colour.

The water gathers into a rapid,
Destroying everything in its path,
Splashing up over the banks,
As it reaches a reservoir,
My anger is no more.

Daniel Adams (13)

A TYPICAL TEENAGER'S LIFE

I feel trapped in my own home,
Nothing to do, not allowed out.
People treat me like a kid.
I'll crack soon, I'll shout or slam doors.
No one understands,
If they treat me like a kid, I'll act like one.

It's not fair; my little sister gets less homework.
I need my sleep, but how can I do that with all this work?
How can I have a social life with all this studying?
People treat me too grown up.
I'm not ready to grow up yet.
Can't people treat me as a teen?
I'm not ready to grow up, but I'm too old to be treated like a kid.
Help me please!

I feel confused,
My mum shouts to grow up!
My dad shouts that I'm only a kid!
If they treated me like a teen,
They wouldn't need to use their voices so loud.
I get angry, shout back or slam doors.
I need to get out, I feel trapped in my own home,
Nothing to do, not allowed out.

Elizabeth Rowe (13)

THINK!

One day I was walking down a lane,
A butterfly came gliding through the air.
A girl, my age, with a net on a cane,
Came rushing past yelling, 'This one is rare.'
I stopped in my tracks and turned around,
With a swish and a flick she'd caught it.
She seemed so excited at what she had found;
She said, 'With my butterfly collection, this will fit!'

Wondering how anyone could think this way, I stood,
A growing hatred welling up inside.
I yelled, 'Killing butterflies - I don't know how you could.'
'Easy,' she said, 'you stick a pin through its side.'
I stood looking at her with so much disbelief,
And I thought to myself, is she for real?
All insects from this beautiful place - does she have to thieve?
In doing so, the beauty of this place, she does steal.

Coming out of my trance, I snatched at the box,
In which the poor creature was held.
He soared freely, towards sunlight, as I undid the locks,
Some nasty things said as the girl yelled.
But she quietened as he began to grow,
How the tables had turned as he reached our size.
'You'll look nice pinned to my wall.' he said swooping low,
As he grabbed her and started to rise.

Think! What would you do,
If the creature being tortured was in fact *you!*

Katrina Martin (15)

MY FAMILY

I would like you to meet my family,
First there's my dad,
He's the best dad in the world,
Yer he's my dad.
My dad is well smart
And of course he is so funny,
Yer he's my dad,
My only dad.

Then my mum,
She's a great mum,
No one else could replace her,
Of course she's my mum.
My mum acts like a wonder mum,
She's always busy,
Busy, busy, busy,
Of course she's my mum.

And then my brother,
Yer my bro,
He's older than me
But only by three.
He would buy me sweets
Oh yer, and ice cream.
He isn't very clean, but,
Yer, he's my bro.

Now that's my family and I love them all.

Kimberley Perrin (13)

THROUGH THE EYES OF A TEENAGER

Being a teenager sure isn't easy,
Acne, spots and feeling wheezy,
No more playing on the street,
Embarrassing moments feel the heat
Different clothes for different teens,
Designer gear, trainers and jeans
Some teens start taking drugs
Others run wild get known as thugs
Some of us are really quite nice
While the others have to pay the price
Some skip school, watch the telly
McDonald's fast food in their belly
Being a teen, one of my fears
Being a teen, six whole years
Some teens behind bars
Smoking drugs and stealing cars
Try to do the best with your time
Get into sport, don't do crime
These years are important try and do well
Head for a career, not a prison cell.

David James Greene

KNIVES OF HATE

Icy mountains stab into the darkness
Piercing the endless clear black sky
Frosted stars are pin pricks in the swirl of tumbling snowflakes
They spiral in the lurching heights.

Iron boulders litter the deadened slopes
Crevices gape in the mountain's wounded sides
Caves bore down towards its frozen heart
It stands strong but rots in ancient malice.

The moon gazes with his steely stare
Towards the bleeding tears in his treasured sky
He hates the blades that score its scars
And longs them shattered to broken dust.

For many years they've waged this war
A battle where each opponent is as decayed as the other
Each crumble in the absence of love or thought
They care not for the others hurt.

Bridie B Murphy (13)

TEENAGE WEEK

It's hard to wake up,
When school is on your mind,
Friends, clothes and make-up,
When school is on your mind.

    It's fun to have a friendly smile,
    When you're out with your mates,
    Talking, laughing, worrying about style,
    When you're out with your mates.

        It's hard to have a good old rest,
        When there is piles of homework to do,
        Mobiles, hair, not a vest,
        When there is piles of homework to do.

            It's nice to finally go to sleep,
            When a busy week is over,
            Rest, nap and count sheep,
            When a busy week is over.

Beth Hind (15)

THE REVOLT OF THE TREES

This is the tale of a woodcutter man.
Chopped wood in the forest, with an axe in the hand.
Travelled to market to sell in the town.
The goodness of the forest hauled by evil hands.

He didn't believe in the power of the land.
No reserves of goodness he held in his mind.
Cutting trees without mercy to his axe's demand.
To travelling folk he would not be so kind.

And the trees looked on to his strong wood house . . .

Branch by branch they tore it down,
And sowed the land around with flowers.
And when he got home, and saw what they'd done
He reached for his axe but it was gone.
He gazed out in horror to the things around.
Razed to the ground, his home scattered about.
He raised his head towards the sun,
And saw what he'd become -
    Not a stone cast to sea,
    Not a bird of sky he,
    Not a stream of the lee,
    But he stood a tree.

Mark Charlesworth (15)

HOPE

A tiny golden bird,
Sparkling like a scrap of sunshine,
Glides effortlessly through the endless expanse of sky.

As it darts behind the clouds,
The world is filled with sinister shadows
And a thick, suffocating melancholy blankets the Earth.

At last, it reappears,
A flash of gold heralding its return
And warm, glittering feathers caress the saddest of hearts.

Lizzy Huitson (14)

YOU

I think of you day and night,
Wondering where you are,
You say you love me,
But you're never there,
Where are you?

I wait on the streets,
While the wind, as cold as ice, passes,
I feel the cold,
But I do not feel the warmth of your hands
And you're still not there,
Just waiting, and waiting.

My love for you is like,
An everlasting rosebud,
Though your rose is black,
As black as night in the sky above,
I go weak at the knees,
While you stand with no care.

I wait for you in darkness, alone,
I watch and listen,
But no sign of you,
You leave me stranded in despair,
You don't care,
You break my heart and still I can't stop
Loving you.

Hayley Lucy Reeves (14)

A Night In A Teenager's Life

You watch TV, that you can't live without,
Sit down on the sofa, relax with a drink,
You watch EastEnders without a blink.
The Simpsons come on, you are going to burst,
But The Simpsons come first.
After an hour your bladder is full,
You run upstairs as fast as you can,
You come back down, jump on the couch,
Find your brother slumping around,
A slap on the head, a boot to the bum,
Upstairs he goes, telling your mum.
It's 12 o'clock now, you're feeling slumped,
Your mum comes down and gives you a tug,
You climb up the stairs, roll into bed,
'Goodnight, sweet dreams, you big sleepyhead!'

Olivia Bridge (13)

A Poem About Teenage Life

T   is for the tempers you have at home.
E   is for my rap idol Eminem.
E   is for your excited mood before you go to a disco.
N   is for the nagging you receive from your parents.
A   is for your annoying brothers and sisters.
G   is for the grimy spots that pop up all over your face.
E   is for your lack of enthusiasm towards homework.

L   is for your loud music you play in your bedroom.
I   is for the illnesses I fake to get out of going to school.
F   is for your fantastic mum that's always there for you.
E   is for the extremely bad hairdays I seem to have every day.

Lindsey Anderson (13)

MY PERFECT WORLD

My world,
A perfect place to live in,
No pain,
No suffering,
Everybody lives in peace
And enjoys having their freedom,
No vandalism,
No burglars or murderers,
So that everyone is safe,
Without needing walls,
Or barriers,
So there's no need for protection,
The world is beautiful,
So protect it
And help to make it a better place.

David Foulstone (13)

JOURNEY

I wonder how my life would be,
Maybe, wondering around feeling lonely.

I wonder if I'll ever find
Wonderful people who are perfect and kind,

Will life find me a happy place
Feeling beautiful with a pretty face,

I hope I'm strong through trouble and strife
I wish I find my travel through life,

A great story of a place unknown
A journey that is hard, as hard as a stone.

Nicola Hold (14)

SUNSTREAM

'Slay the spirit!'
The Jay bird cried.
'Come to the Indian,'
Cried the beaded moccasin.
'Swim with the sea's claw,'
The sailor man called.

'Come to me my honeys,
Come fly with the striped vee-bee.
Come to run with the morning's breath,
Sleep protected by angel's wings,
Call with the voice, like His chosen one.
All goodness, peace and serenity.'
The Sun-man secretly whispered.

In reply the hunter carved,
Into the evening's stone, the likes of the Earth.
'In morning's call, and midday's run,
The ancient worshipping.
Kneel down to the All-Mother,
Kiss the stripy Hubber-gubber's scent.'

The reader the scene of never loved before,
He a-trembled from the toe to the hair.
For this chant was the Sunstream,
The trees whispered call;

The Mmadacascan wolf howled.
'Call with the Lords of Never;
Hum with the first hummingbird's hum,'
The old, river-mud hippo called.
'Call of the wild, call of the come,
Call of the way, summon the sun.'

'A manifesto of misogony,
Of the ocean's wildest dreams,'
This is the song of der Fuhrer,
The leader's Hindu song.
The reader knelt down and slaved,
And prayed for Macbeth's regiside.

Claire Shepherd (14)

DREAMING

Shutting your windows on the day,
Your problems are calmly washed away.

Stepping on the marshmallow clouds,
Slowly dodging the glistening stars.

Leaving your troubles in the past,
The week is moving all too fast.

Warmly tucked into bed,
Nothing to think of or to dread.

Enveloped in the beat of your heart,
Sweetly in the land of nod.

In a land of peace and hope,
Your chance to relax and mope.

Feeling the bouncy green grass,
No need for the dream to quickly pass.

Following the bold rainbow,
To find your personal pot of gold.

Lifting your moist eyelids, waking up,
The sun gently blazes to tell you, get up!

Samantha Tumelty (14)

MONSTERS

Monsters in the night,
Really hate the light
There are small ones, big ones
And ones that can't bear the sight
They come while you sleep,
Then they begin to weep,
Like big babies in a zoo.

There was a rumour going round,
That they sleep in the ground,
And while they sleep,
They begin to walk
And then begin to talk.

They begin to scream,
Then begin to yell,
Causing such a fright.
In your sleep they come for you
And say to you, 'Goodnight.'
You try to wake
But something's there, keeping eyes shut tight
You try to struggle and to fight,
But something holds you tight,
You find yourself falling,
Drifting out of sight.

Patricia Townsend (14)

PURGATORY

Renegade emotions fly through my brain,
Uncontrollable, worsened by their visibility.
Skin deepens with natural rouge
And boils with panic and embarrassment.
Clothes constrict painfully.
Boys gulp speechlessly, fish out of water, suffocating.

An ever-changing body creates an ever-changing hell.
Betrayed by our actions,
Condemned by parents for 'unchristian thoughts'.
We pay penitence for Adam's sin,
Puberty is a teen's purgatory.

Michael David Wood (15)

Don't Look Back In Anger

Flags from every window
Taken down with regret
As the floods of tears
Drop at the sound of a whistle

A nation united in sadness
As our country walks
Empty handed and down
As our world ends

But there's nothing to fear
Twenty-three heroes got us that far
Goal after goal they scored
Bringing smiles to our mighty England

A day we shall remember
Forever in our hearts
The day we lost the cup
But gained a nation

Football,
It's a passion for life
And just because we've lost it now
Remember,
There's always next time lads!

Laura Eve Wood (14)

FEAR POSSESSES ME

It is cold.
It is dark.
I can't breathe.
Fear's snarling jaws and
Huge, sharp claws creeping up behind me.
Owls look down with great, wide eyes,
Telling me fear's close behind.
The adrenaline is pumping,
My heart is thumping.
My eyes dart round the wide, dark forest.
Fog appears in front of me rustling the leaves.
I feel it's damp presence.
Fear's eyes appear in front of me through the forest dark.
It's dagger-like glare stares straight through me,
Looking at my soul.
It scars me with its claws,
I fall; once again fear has won my mind.
Fear fades in front of me,
Nothing's there,
I'm all alone.

Andrea Taylor (13)

DOG

Is my favourite, life saving,
Supporting sight, a
Faithful saint. Is a
Fierce hunter who seeks
For the guilty. Playful

But destructive little things,
Their pale soft fur stroking
Your smooth skin.
Pampered pooch trimmed
And decorated. A sleek, thin

Racing machine, bred to fight
And kill in the pit.
A fierce and feared
Protector of property. Competing
With their own blood, racing

Towards victory. Gathering
The harvest, shot ducks and rabbits.
Mankind's true friend. Always
Honest towards their masters.
Dogs are, dogs are.

Fahimah Araf (13)

WHAT'S GOING ON?

Your sister's annoying
Your parents treat you like a kid
What's going on?
You've got acne
And you smell too
What's going on?
The geography teacher hates you
And you hate him back
What's going on?
Your hair's greasy every day
Even after it's been washed
What's going on?
You feel depressed
You look at boys in a whole different light,
Let's just call it,
Puberty
You'll get over it!

Helen Law (14)

THE WITCH'S PROLOGUE

Her hair was extremely long
But not in strength was she strong
The talent was well hidden
Among many books that she had written
For she could cast and blast
Many people into the past
Her best was the best of all
That worked even if her victim was very tall
Also hidden was her own past
In an imagination so vast
It was easy to lose all time
She didn't care to drop her grape from the vine
Her boots were worn and tattered
The mind was bruised and battered
Her clothes were so wild
She had had them since she was a child
Upon her neck a pendant lay
Given by my mother she used to say
A star and circle upon a piece of twine
That was usually fine
She never had men in her life
For she would end up with a knife
In his throat
But his body would float in a moat
And she would be burned at the stake
But not death would it make
Was it black or white,
Dark or light?
Well it was dark and black
Fore no one could kill a witch.

Julia Hart (13)

LIVE AS ONE IN LOVE

Have you seen the sunrise
Promising your daylight
When all you need is to share your thoughts around?

Did you ever think that
Life was just a highway
A never-ending road of lonely days?

There are times we cry
And reach out to the sky
For the strength we need
To keep our head up high.

Have you seen the sunset
Fade beneath the rain clouds?
Have you ever chased your dreams away?

Did you ever feel like
Love was just an island?
You can't stay and survive it on your own.

There are times when I
Need to reach inside
For the strength I need
To hold my head up high

All we have to do now
Is love one another
Sisters and brothers
Can all live as one
All we have to do now
Is show one another
We all need each other
To live as one in love.

Kavitha Suhumar (14)

BEST FRIENDS!

Best friends are the best!
They stand by you through thick and thin.
Regardless of the country,
They will be there,
Best friends are just the best!

Best friends are brill!
You can tell them about your first love,
About all your problems,
No matter what, they will always be there,
Best friends are just the best!

Best friends are great!
If you fall out with them,
Everything will be resolved,
And you'll be the best of friends again.
Best friends are just great!

Friends are forever!

Nyarji Lomuro (13)

MY WORLD

Somewhere in the world there will be happiness,
Elsewhere in the world there will be sadness,
Somewhere in the world there will be love,
Elsewhere in the world there will be hate,
But in my world everyone likes each other.

Somewhere in the world children will be playing,
Elsewhere in the world children will be fighting,
Somewhere in the world children will be laughing,
Elsewhere in the world children will be crying,
But in my world children stick together.

Somewhere in the world there will be war,
Elsewhere in the world there will be peace,
Somewhere in the world people will be hindering each other,
Elsewhere in the world people will be helping each other,
But in my world everyone loves each other.

In my world everyone likes each other,
Because in my world everyone loves each other,
In my world everyone sticks together,
But also in my world everyone is content with what they have.

Tracie Watson (13)

DECISIONS

Who shall I choose?
Where shall I go?
Which direction?
I do not know!

Who shall I live with?
Who should I invite?
Shall I bring him?
Don't know, I might.

Which colour's the best?
Which friend should I call?
Should I pick them up, when they fall?

Decisions, decisions fill my head
I may just go to sleep instead.

Goodnight.

Claudia Obiedzinski (14)

DON'T YOU WANT TO COME WITH ME, UNDER THE SEA?

Don't you want to come with me?
Under the sea, under the sea
To see the different fish go by
Instead of all the birds in the sky
Under the sea, under the sea.

Don't you want to come with me?
Under the sea, under the sea
Where different types of plants roam free
Oh why, oh why, don't you come with me?
Under the sea, under the sea.

Don't you want to come with me?
Under the sea, under the sea
I'll see all the wonders by myself
And leave you wondering, on the shelf
Under the sea, under the sea.

Don't you want to come with me?
Under the sea, under the sea
I'm asking you, this is your last chance
To swim with the fishes and then dance
Under the sea, under the sea.

Laura C Williams (15)

SUMMERTIME

In summertime, I wake up to the sun shining and the birds singing.
The air is warm and light,
The grass feels fresh and crispy beneath my feet.
I can hear happy cries of children playing.
Summertime is a happy and joyous time.

Helena Olmos (13)

I'M ALL MIXED UP

I'm confused
I don't know what to do,
One minute I'm happy, the next, I'm sad,
What's happening to me?

I'm all mixed up
I don't know what to think or feel anymore,
Is this normal?
Is there something wrong with me,
Am I a freak?

Someone please help me,
Please tell me if it's normal to feel like the way I am.

I'm all mixed up,
Sometimes I have self-confidence, sometimes I don't.

Somebody please help,
Is there anybody out there who can help me
And feels the way in what I'm feeling at the moment?
I don't know what to do anymore.

Please help
I'm all mixed up.

Bethany Horrocks (14)

TEENAGERS

We worry about anything,
Which boy we fancy or who is the cutest in Blue,
We have arguments with our parents or best friend,
But then we worry about odd things like spots,
Hair, make-up and fashion
And all those things come to us as we are
Teenagers!

Karen Symonds-Tate (13)

STINGER

MC Scorpio sting like a scorpion
Sting like a black one
It's hot you'd better hold on
I'm getting poked by a Pokémon
Going digital like Digimon
I go solo with the Scorpion Soul
I dig so deep I dig like a mole
Making lyrics in dark holes
Bump and flex those heavy goals
Cursing them grimy trolls
I'm on a roll.

I roll so fast down those blue hills
Making sure the pop never spills
I throw a mad tantrum like a mad drill
I'm so hot you are gonna grill
I'm taking all those fakes out my till
Those fakes will never pay the bill (cha-ching)
Watch how I sting
Come to me if you want more bling
Bling bling on the telephone ring.

Ms Dynamite is alright
Shine the night with your Dynamite
She takes you to a brand new height
She can dig you out like a iron-might
That's right, can't fight, won't fight
If you can't do this right
Then get out of my sight.

Marcus Williams (15)

My Family

My grannie
My grannie is my only grannie and she is great,
she is always making jokes
and watches all the programs that I like with me.
If I hurt myself by falling she cleans me up
by putting on plaster on it.
She also listens to music with me and wears flowery skirts.
She has also got a lot of plants which she cares for.

My auntie
My auntie is also a great person,
She buys me things and looks after the dog.
Her favourite person in the whole world is her mum.
My auntie has a lot of cuddly toys.
Her favourite film is James Bond.
Her favourite singer is Ronan Keating.

My uncle
My uncle is also a great person
and is always buying me things and making jokes.
He is involved in a lot of things
with the buses and he also works for them
and is a great enthusiast.

My dad
My dad is a person that is great
and will do anything if you ask him.
He also buys me things for my computer and other things,
he is the best dad.
My dad is also someone that helps you out if you need help.

Paul Grubb (14)

MY DESTINY

Outside the room in alphabetical order,
I'm right at the front trembling with fear.
I never imagined that this day would come,
And now finally it's here.

Directed to go in the room,
I'm told to be seated,
Anxiously facing the brick wall in front,
While the others entered the hall.

Retrieving my paper,
Chills run down my spine.
'You may begin!' he calls,
And so here I go.

A . . . B . . . C . . . or D . . .
What is my destiny?

Mobeena Afridi (14)

SPOTS

Spots, we all get them
And we all hate them.
When you first become a teenager you think it's great,
But when you get spots being a teenager is what you really hate.
To everyone else it's just a spot,
But to us it's a mighty shock.
You just get rid of one spot,
Then a couple of days later another one appears.
Being a teenager with spots is terrible.
Wouldn't life be great if we didn't have spots?
Because a life without spots
Would mean there was one less thing
For us teenagers to worry about.

Steven Brackenridge (13)

DOLPHINS

Dolphins swimming in the swirly blue sea
Creating swirls of happiness and joy
Slender bodies swishing, making patterns
Swirling with a whoosh

Dorsal fins steering through the sea as they swim
Magnificent tail fins, for driving through the water
Looking for food whilst they swim
With immense power and enormous cries of happiness

As they swim in large shoals
They play with fun and intelligence
By following each other
They communicate through their own language
Creating immense joy here and there.

Sarah Stott (14)

WAR

A brutal activity with the aftermath of mass devastation.
Fighting for wealth, power and supremacy.
It creates years of sorrow and mourning.

Swords swinging, cannons booming.
The pull of a trigger could mean tragic fatality.
Battling is for victory,
Although real triumph would be when all wars are redundant.

Imagine a world without war.
Happiness, harmony and universal humanity.
A world without conflict.
Is it possible?

Helen Moore (13)

MY TWIN SISTER, MY FRIEND

My sister's name is Becky,
She acts like she's three years old,
She'd sit by the fire while I'd be freezing cold.
I love my sister really; I think she's really sweet,
Her favourite food is pizza, which she loves to eat.

She really is quite clever though,
She plays the harp, violin and the piano.
Music resounds around the house,
Whilst I, of course, am as quiet as a mouse!

To have a twin sister like Becky,
Makes me feel very lucky.
She'd do anything for me,
Whatever it may be,
I love my sister Becky.

Hannah Watson (14)

WHICH WAY?

There are two sides to a person,
One can be afraid and hurting
And never go out flirting,
But just remember . . .

There are two sides to a person,
One can be lively and daring,
Also loving and caring,
But just remember . . .

Face your fears and live your dreams,
Let people know you're not afraid,
Become familiar with new things
And always hold your head up high.

Kirsty Glaister (14)

LOVE ISN'T EASY

Why do you always have to go?
When will the day come when we can just be alone?
My heart beats for you inside
For the day when you're back by my side
As time takes its toll
It's you I want to hold
When will you come back, it's been so long
I'm sorry, I let you go,
But what can you expect, you never wanted to see me
But now that's in the past
I want this relationship to last
But in the end it has turned out okay
'Cause now you're back and here to stay.
I will always love you no matter what.

Joanne Cox (15)

THE MONSTER UNDER MY BED

There's a monster under my bed
I woke up this morning
I couldn't believe what it said.
'I've never heard so much snoring!'
Today, school was so boring.
Half my pencil's gone
From which I was gnawing
Listening to my teachers going on.
Upstairs I heard loud bellows
The monster's hands covering his head
'I'm an ugly fellow'
Said the monster, from under my bed.

Christina Hill

TESS

I'm a teenager, at least I think,
Everything is out of sync.

I just don't know how I feel,
I really wish this wasn't real.

I go with my friend to hang out,
But suddenly I want to shout.

I'm angry, 'You are such a berk,
Stop acting like a total jerk!'

He answers, 'Hey, what's up with you?'
I haven't got the slightest clue.

I storm away to be on my own,
I just want to be left alone.

On my own, I think today,
About what made me act that way.

So I go back, to see if he's there,
He is, and so we stand and stare.

Then I go forward, avoid his eyes,
And woodenly apologise.

We're mates again, and we go to a club,
Cos we're too young to get into a pub.

As we enter through the door,
I see a girl on the dance floor.

She dances to the music's beat,
Waves her arms and moves her feet.

Her hair is black and goes straight down,
Her eyes are of the darkest brown.

I walk over and ask if she,
Would ever want to go with me.

She smiles, 'You can call me Tess,
And if you want to, okay, yes!'

Dale Smith (13)

A SPECIAL GROUP

You know you have people around you,
Which care and love you;
But the one group is a special group.

You know they will always be there,
They will always stand by you;
Through hard, rough times.

Those people will never leave you,
Will always ring you,
And never forget you.

These people are the most important people,
And you will only have them for a lifetime,
These people are so special to you,
That you will never forget them.

These people are your family . . .
The ones which would not
Replace you, dump you, or let you go.
I will always love and care
Through hard times.
We will stick together through thick and thin,
Because I love my family so much;
That I would not replace them.

Because they are my family . . .

Keira Robinson

HORSES

Horses everywhere. Horses galloping through the moors.
Horses flying through the air like their mystical ancestor Pegasus.
Horses grazing in the woods. Playing and squealing.
Horses drinking in crystal clear stream and splashing through the river.
Foals cantering and jumping over fallen branches.
Horses stampeding through the glistening snow-topped mountains.
Horses gracefully gallop across the meadows and moors.
Horses rear on the hills while the sun sets.
Horses bucking just for fun.
Far in the distance there is a small thunder getting louder and louder,
There's a herd of horses being chased by a fox.
The fox snapping at the horses' hocks. Horses kick in defence.
Horses are very aggressive, the power comes from the hind quarters.
Ears back, teeth showing,
Horses spin round to avoid violent kicks in the face.
Horses stand their ground. Horses everywhere.

Rachel Ayre (13)

WHEN I HEAR MY MUSIC

When I'm all alone
I turn to my music
My twelve string guitar, is the one I play,
If I choose it

But when my guitar strings break
I can't play my music anymore
Because it sounds like a rake
And dancing becomes a bore

After tuning it
And replacing strings
I think happy thoughts when I hear my music!

Carolyn Payne (14)

FLOWERS

Flowers are sweet,
Flowers are pretty.
They grow,
Start off small
Then blossom into a big flower.

Flowers make places colourful,
Flowers make places nice.
In gardens, houses, fields,
And many more places.

Flowers also save a couple,
A man gives a lady a bunch of flowers,
She feels happy and pleased.
Flowers are lovely and
Even though we don't know it,
They make our world a pleasant place.

Sophie Louise Greenhough

ANGER

Anger is a fireball burning in my stomach
Only my good friends can dowse its flames
They are the solution to my burning anger
Somewhere in their stomach they hold the fire too
So watch out when you're on the street,
The flames might get to you
These burning flames are everywhere,
There is no safe place
So when you go out and about
Be sure to wear a happy face.

Danny Edwards (13)

The Happy Years

Now you're twelve, teens next year,
Booze, boys bring up fear,
Don't even mention career.

Teenager now you've met your fate,
Period pains up for debate,
Who to call your new best mate?

Now you're fourteen, smoking and drink,
Both of which make your breath stink,
Not nice for kissing, just think.

Teenager, still signs start to show,
Hormones, breasts and genitals grow,
The deadly periods flow.

Now you're sixteen, loving a boy,
Sex to you is all about joy,
It's better to be all coy.

Teenager at seventeen, school out of mind,
University and college, I think you'll find
The people there I hear are quite kind.

Now you're eighteen, marriage and a kid,
Being attached to a guy called Sid.

Adulthood next!

Melanie Austin (13)

Anger

My anger is like a floor,
Straight, rough and hard to damage.
My anger is a fierceful sadness
People constantly stepping on it.
Making it worse.

I cry, I shout, I scream 'Silence!'
No one hears.
They just keep stepping
Ignoring the floor's feelings.
Making it worse.

Nicole Binns (13)

WE'RE ONLY FIFTEEN

When I started secondary school I made new friends
And we promised never to do drugs,
Or get so drunk we would pass out,
But no one took notice, no one.

I sit at school and look at my friends,
People who used to be special to me,
Drifting away, to their own little world,
Their precious minds stolen by drugs and alcohol.

'It makes me feel better,' they say,
'I only did it the once,' they say,
But didn't you ever get taught,
One time can last a lifetime?

'I'll stop,' they say,
'It's only a bit of fun,' they say
Then they're not in school the next day and you wonder,
Did they overdose last night?

I look at the world through my eyes and ask myself,
What is the world coming to?
We're only fifteen,
We've got our whole lives ahead of us,
We're only fifteen.

Gemma Balch (15)

COLOURS OF THE WORLD

Red is danger, red is pain,
red is the love that we wish to gain.

Yellow is happy, yellow is bright,
yellow is the sun, the morning light.

Pink is girly, pink is nice,
pink is the colour of sugar mice.

Green is neutral, green is calm,
green is a clover, a lucky charm.

Orange is sunset, orange is loud,
orange is the colour of the evening cloud.

Purple is thunder, purple is a grape,
purple is the colour of a wizard's cape.

Blue is icy, blue is cold,
good luck for brides with something old.

Every colour is something - wow!
Be grateful for them all right now!

Jess Twitchin (14)

SUMMER

As I look out of my window,
At the sea so blue,
The sun so yellow,
I never feel glum.

The sand so soft and shiny,
The children skipping by,
The kites beginning to fly,
In the high, cloudy sky.

And I think to myself,
I live in a wonderful place
And a big smile
Comes to my rosy-red face.

Emma Lawrence (13)

SOMEONE WORSE OFF THAN ME

I do not walk upon my feet
Like others in this cobbled street
I have two wheels, one left, one right
Arms swiftly propel me out of sight
My legs simply won't perform this straightforward errand

Walking certainly isn't a chore for me
Legs don't ache from dawn till dusk
I have a seat of my own
You could call it my own personal throne

Family are restricted as to what they can do
Steps are all we see
Hoisting me up them, a definite task for two

Chess and draughts is what I'm really about
Pop music is my thing no doubt
Reading books is what I love to do
Please give me a chance to get to know you

Swimming, athletics and hockey too
Sixty metres is what I really want to master
A striving sportsman I hope to be

People worse off that me I notice
People worse off that me I see
People worse off than me I witness
There is always someone worse off than me.

Carl Healey (15)

THE END

Tears, falling like raindrops,
    Then turning to dust.
A smile fading slowly,
    Like paint into rust.

Laughter, an echo,
    Of a happier day.
One when you're there
    And had not turned away.

A mist in my eyes,
    Like early morning dew.
The same in my mind,
    When I think about you.

The pain and the hurt,
    My heart torn in two.
But you've nothing to say.
    So there's nothing I can do.

I remember the day,
    We spent in the rain.
But I know it won't happen,
    Ever again.

I've tried to forget you,
    With each passing hour,
But with me losing you,
    I lost all will and all power.

A door slowly closes in my life,
    My soul breaks down to cry,
I watch the rain on the window
    And softly whisper goodbye . . .

Kiri Bashford (15)

THE TEACHER

As he hurriedly enters the vicinity
We immediately see his immensity
As he stoops through the door,
We hear the thuds on the floor
This must be the legendary green giant

Here he comes to wreck the day,
His complexion resembling flaky, dry clay
Our punishment is nigh,
Despite how hard we try
We will never please him sufficiently

As you sit there, saturated in his slaver
You try to ignore his inane blabber,
His animosity towards me,
May lead to an injury
Unless he considers his reprimands.

Alex Moore (14)

PARENTS

Parents are an interesting lot,
They tell us what's right and what's not.

Parents always moan and groan
Especially if we are late coming home!

Parents do not understand,
When their son or daughter,
Is low and down.

Parents are an interesting lot
and we still love them dearly,
Whether we like it or not!

Rebecca Gordon (13)

MY WORLD

My world is like a whirlpool,
Spinning round and round,
My world is like a planet,
Never to be found.

My world is like a cheetah
As fast as you can get,
My world is like a dream
And I haven't woken yet.

My world is like a rocket,
Shooting off up high,
My world is like a hurricane,
Making people die.

My world is like a greyhound,
Racing round a track,
My world is like a boomerang,
Always coming back.

My world is like a speedboat,
Helping those in need,
My world is like a sprinter,
Always in the lead.

My world is like a board game,
Running out of time,
But I like my world just as it is,
Because my world is mine.

Heather Parry (13)

YOU'RE SPECIAL TO ME

Every day I see you,
Always there for me,
You've been there for all my life,
It was clearly meant to be.

Do you remember the fun we had
And that time I started to cry?
Let's not lose what we've got,
Please don't say goodbye.

Even though we're older,
I still look up to you,
It was you, who taught me how to laugh,
You made my dreams come true.

What more could I ask from my special friend,
Who has never let me down,
Who I've never had to fight and scowl with,
Who never made me frown?

Although sometimes we drifted apart,
You never went too far,
But when these times came about,
I always looked to the stars.

So you can see when I'm hurt,
You're always there to mend,
A broken heart that can only be fixed,
By my bestest ever friend.

Emma Duggan (15)

REFUGEES

Every minute someone runs away,
From a country who's at war all day,
They take all they can,
Except their man,
Who has to stay and fight,
All day and night,
Women and children scream,
Praying to God to turn it into a dream,
In some countries it's all there,
Things that no human could bare,
Dead bodies on the floor,
Their blood splashed onto the door,
Those who are left to get away,
Are confused with nothing to say,
They escape to better countries,
Where they hope to start again
And forget all the pain.

Yousafa Hazara (13)

MY UNCLE

My uncle he's loony,
he acts all weird and gooney.
He'll race around on rollerskates,
and has teenage rock band mates.
When we go to school,
all the kids think he's cool.
Because he rides a motorbike,
he even wows the bully called Mike.
If I ever had a choice,
I'd never change my uncle.
He's the best from all the rest,
my loony gooney uncle.

Kazan Tawfiq (14)

WANNABE

The way he wears his hair
Makes me want to sit and stare
The way he walks
Something for all the girls to stalk
He's so fine he makes them gawk

He's tall not small
He makes all the cars stall
He catches the ball
Everything stops
Oh it's just him
The one with the grin

Maybe he's a supermodel
Well he does love to dawdle

Maybe he's a rockstar
He's got the moves
That goes with his grooves.

As he walks he slips and trips
His pants rip at the seam
Which makes all the girls scream

He screeches and squeals in a broken voice
He runs to his haven
Where he will be saven

He's not a supermodel
Although he does dawdle
He's not a rock star
Because he's got no real groove
And he doesn't know how to move
He's just him
The one with the grin
He's just the wannabe.

Sonja Burch (15)

SHE WANTS TO BE LIKE THOSE PEOPLE

A girl I knew once told me
'I don't want to turn out like you!
I want to be the cool type
And I'll do whatever I have to do.'

The clothes she wears are just not her
Those short, tight clothes, she hates,
But wearing them makes her look flash
Just like her popular mates.

'I hang around with the guys,' she says
'Even if it's not me.
I've got to show the world,' she says
'I'm the coolest there can be.'

She makes sure that she's always late
For meetings, work and school.
If she goes early and waits a while
She just won't look cool.

She answers back with attitude
And shows everyone where she stands.
Why her parents say, 'Be back by 8!'
She neither listens nor understands.

She makes herself anorexic
Just to fit into a size six.
She wants to be amongst those girls
Who are called the groovy chicks.

Fagging looked cool, so she started that too
She always believed she was right.
The fagging got to her heart and lungs
And she died the very next night.

Well now I can say back to that girl,
'I don't want to end up like you.
I want to be smart and intelligent
And I'll do whatever I have to do!'

Raihana Mawjee (15)

ALL THIS STRESS

All these exams coming up,
For my summer report.
I haven't got a lot of time,
So I'm going to make this poem short.

So much to revise for,
Especially for my history.
And for my HE,
Learning how to roll our pastry.

I'll have to buy some paint,
To do some of my art.
So much to do,
So where so I start?

I'll have to learn about the body,
For my PE.
But what I'm really nervous about,
Is my HE.

So now I'm going to revise,
To get a good summer report.
So I hope you enjoyed my poem,
I told you it would be short.

Sarah Comfort (15)

AS I LOOK OUT OF MY WINDOW

As I look out of my window I see,
Trees rustling in the summer's breeze,
As if they're trying to tell me their secrets never told,
Deep down in the soil their roots spread out,
As does their knowledge too
And all the time their wisdom grows,
Mine is growing too!

As I look out of my window,
I see birds soaring high up in the sky,
I feel as though they're trying to tell me,
The expeditions of their days,
When they're flying in the air they seem so free,
But when they're put in cages,
Their joy seems to flee.

As I look out of my window,
I see foxes darting around with such amazing ease,
I sometimes think they're trying to tell me,
About fierce battles they have fought,
With wicked men on horseback,
And their bloodthirsty hounds,
They chase these beautiful creatures,
So they hide underground.

Lawrence Keath (13)

NO SIX WEEKS HOLIDAY

What if we had no six weeks?
No time to sleep,
No time to play,
No time for a holiday,
What if we had no six weeks?

Simon Elwell (14)

THE FAMOUS

They drive around,
In their flash cars.
Who are they?
They are the stars!

Designer clothes
Are all they wear,
It must be so good
Being way up there!

It must feel great
Being one of the best,
They say it's not
They all need a rest.

They get no privacy,
The papers tell lies,
It gets too much,
They just want to die.

Some of them do -
It gets too much.
Booze and drugs,
People such . . .

As Marilyn Monroe,
She was one of the best.
She took too much,
Now at permanent rest.

So it's not so good,
Being way up there.
If you want to be famous,
Just beware!

Sarah O'Leary (15)

ADULTS

Adults just don't understand what it is like to be our age.
They were our age so long ago; don't mention this, it turns to rage.
The rage then turns to laughter and we get the same old phrase.
'In my day, we had to walk there and back,' so listen you
                                        may get some praise.
They don't understand mobile phones or how to talk in code.
Nor do they get why we always dress smartly and like to
                                        live in nice abode.
They can't understand our maths homework, so it's no
                                        use asking for advice.
It's all too difficult these days, but a tutor comes at a very high price.
They say that rap is for people who can't sing, but we all
                                        know it is good.
Well what can we say about their type of music?
We don't like it, but then again who would?
We all seem so different and like totally opposite things,
But really it's what kind of people we are and the quality
                                        of our upbringing.
We have got to remember that they were once kids; they
                                        did all the same as us.
Only a different generation, a different life,
They had to walk, we catch the bus.

Lorah Campbell (15)

UNTITLED

You use me,
You hurt me,
You bitch behind my back,
Sometimes I feel like giving you a whack.

You be nice to my face,
'Oh give me a break!'
I feel like spreading rumours about you too,
But I won't slump to a level as low as you.

You turn people away from me,
Don't lie, you know it's true,
You are so sly, I hope you die,
Because you hurt me through and through.

Everyone thinks you're an angel,
But I know what you're really like,
Why can't they see, what you do to me?
You totally ruin my life.

Laura McCabe (15)

FURTHER REDUCTIONS

They begin to furiously tear
The slanderous and artificial wrapper of their soul
As they entered the wasteland.
Like so many others, leaving common sense
Lynched on a livid banner.
Their life irrelevant.
Numerous brainwashes by the second,
Subliminal nothings, rotting away.
Pride is not a method of payment,
Visa is the indication of respect,
All or nothing.
Can I help? Of course you can,
Can you part exchange a human right?
I have lost my way, get one free, no one cares
In a commercial wasteland.
Don't delay, sell your life away.
Nothing else better to do on a fatigued weekday,
Never-ending, plastic fantastic
Beneath a hypocritical lie
Just one, why not two?
An employed mannequin strongly advises you
To have a nice day.

Michael Kennedy (15)

MY WORLD

My world is different in so many ways
And some people just can't accept it!
I'm different to most and I don't care
Because that's the way I like it.

I like rock music, they like pop
And I like baggy clothes,
They love their rugby and football too
But sports like that I loathe.

Most of the time my world is fun
We have BBQs, picnics and water fights.
Sunbathing in the summer days
And parties in the nights.

The Green Day concert's coming soon
And for that I really can't wait!
It's happening in Cardiff Castle
And I know it's going to be great!

There're loads of concerts and gigs going on
So I'll be there with the girls.
We'll all have fun we always do
So welcome to my world!

Sally Howard (15)

MY FAMILY

My family are not normal
They are not like all the rest
They are so special to me
We never are depressed

My mum is always there for me
And so is my dad
They help me through difficult times
When I'm annoyed and sad

My brother is alright sometimes
Sometimes he thinks he's the best
He thinks he's so popular
But he's just an annoying pest

We all argue over stupid things
But that's what families do
So if you read this poem
This will probably sound familiar to you.

Jenna Watson (14)

A SCHOOL DAY

First lesson,
Maths,
A test to do,
Second lesson,
Geography
Little to do,
Third lesson,
RE,
Worksheets to do,
Fourth lesson,
Science,
Book work to do,
Fifth lesson,
History,
Worksheets and book work to do,
Sixth lesson,
English,
An essay to do,
Home,
A heap of homework to do,
Today,
Far too much to do.

Oliver Butler (13)

CLAIRE

Claire she was a skinny girl
With hair as black as night,
A young and pretty skinny girl,
But always looked a sight.

For Claire she would not eat her food
For fear of getting fat,
But if she doesn't then she will die
But Claire never understood that.

She'd chase her food around her plate
Never do with it what was right.
Her mum and dad explained to her
And they tried with all their might.

Soon after Claire got very weak
And her friends stopped going round.
For when they did it was only
The pale and lifeless Claire they found.

And when her life got sacrificed
For the sake of one small snack
Stop and look and ask yourself . . .
Am I *really* getting fat?

Vicki Gibson (15)

ILLUSION

My eyes are covered once again,
Whose hands are responsible?
I do not want to be restricted,
Am I really that controllable?

The truth is just behind that wall,
But can I reach it in time?
It's harder than I thought it would be,
Will the truth ever be mine?

I want to break the barrier,
Don't keep me in this cell.
You cannot hide it forever,
I'll break free from this Hell.

Reality cannot be a secret,
I cannot live in delusion,
Take away everything fake,
Take away the illusion.

Samia Malik (13)

UNTITLED

I'm now thirteen
And very hard it may seem.
I just want to be out,
But everyone has a doubt
I don't want to stay in
But people think it's a sin,
It's part of growing up
And that I've got to do
From day to day
I'm learning the way
Mum always says 'Don't dare',
But I know I'm to take care
I'll try my best
And not follow the rest
Stay away from drugs,
'Cause they're for mugs
Do well at school,
And stop acting the fool
Life's a gamble, it's like tossing a dice,
But all I hope for is something nice!

Charlotte McMahon (13)

MY SADDEST DAYS

It's not fair, I feel so sombre,
No more do I care, to my despair,
I feel so sad and think why me?
For when I think about it, I feel no glee.

I need to let it out, I start to cry,
Oh why can't I be normal I face facts and sigh,
I think of happy times, life's not too bad,
Especially when, you have the world's best mum and dad.

My mind's adrift, I cannot think,
The sadness creeps back, my face turns pink,
Once more again, I start to cry,
I need to talk to someone, but whom? I sigh.

I'll have to wait, till the right time and place,
To tell - I don't know who - right to their face,
I'll write a letter, maybe I could,
I think it'll be better, I think I should.

I've written a letter, I start to shake,
I'm scared to give it, the earth seems to quake.
I pluck up my courage, and give them the letter,
I'm glad I've told someone, I feel a lot better.

All of this time, I've been hiding away,
When it could have been over, a year ago today.
I've overcome my problems, and don't hesitate,
To say to people, 'My life's now great!'

Sara Allan (14)

UP THERE'S MY WORLD, I'D LOVE TO BE . . .

I look up at the stars at night,
I stand and look and behold their light
And in those stars I see your face,
Suddenly there, then gone with no trace.
I see your eyes looking down on me,
I feel your love,
Your love is for me,
I feel the warmth from their glow,
I thought that I would let you know,
That when I look into the night sky,
I see my ancestors who had to die.
Up there's my world, I'd love to be . . .
Among the stars - ecstasy!
You and me, holding hands,
Us dancing in the moondust and Uranus sand,
Making friends with the man on the moon,
Visiting Jupiter - hopefully soon!
Flying meteors, shooting stars
Visiting places like Pluto and Mars,
Spinning round on the rings of Saturn,
Trying to observe the constellational patterns,
Writing our names across the sky,
Oh please God, tell my why?
I cannot be up there,
Beyond forces of gravity, defying air,
Up there's my world, I'd love to be . . .
Among the stars - just you and me.

Chloe Hobday (15)

MY MATHEMATICAL MYSTERY

I am ripped from the warmth and security
Of my subconscious' womb,
By the ticking alarming hands of my stern timekeeper.
I lay still and mute in my cradle,
Blinded by a white artificial light
And soaked in an amniotic fluid of misery.
A dense charcoal cloud of algebraic agony
Looms towards me, choking and swallowing the light
On its merciless journey.
Toxic bullets of acid rain pour down
And penetrate my skin, soul and mind,
Slowly and painfully corroding my confidence.
I writhe and buck in a fit of fear,
Like a bewildered insect entangled in an arachnid's web
And lash out maniacally with my limbs
In order to break free from the shackles of quadratic equations.
Incarcerated within the four walls of my sterile, perspex prison,
A venomous, green cocktail of means, modes and medians
Is injected into my veins
Paralysing my muscles, and lulling me into a deep trance.
As I plummet into the funereal depths of the mathematical underworld,
I search for the solution to 'X'.
When will maths plus me equal happiness?

Sarika Thanki (15)

BOYS AND FRIENDS

Who do I choose?
Him or her?
Either way I'm gonna lose

Boys come and go
Whilst friends are true,
They often come in helpful too

I'll choose my friend,
Who's always there,
Whilst boys just don't seem to give a care

Friends come first,
Whilst boys come second
Well, that's what *I* reckon.

Nicola Brennan (14)

TEENAGE ANGST

Glittery clothes and braided hair,
Slumber parties, truth or dare.
Fluffy bunnies, puppy dogs,
Fuzzy chicks and scruffy mogs.
Mum and Dad get quite a shock
While you're listening to rock,
Grunge, nu-metal, the double 'O',
Your eyes are red, your voice is slow.
Your body and mind remain intact,
Although, with him, you make a pact.
My Lord of Darkness, He leaves his mark.
The light is fading, the world is dark.
You signed the clause, no turning back,
Mercy is the thing you lack.
Life's a bitch, it's all a lie,
They're all against you, all must die,
He takes your hand in his great claws
Drawing you to Hell's mighty doors
Eternal pain, they burn alive,
As Satan's slave, only you survive.
Fiery demons torment your friends,
The screams of anguish never end.
Enemies in red-hot chains,
The fire burns and evil reigns.

Natalie Cruddace (13)

WHAT COULD HAVE BECOME!

I often dream of him
When we were still together
Holding hands
Kissing round the corner
Or right in front of friends
We weren't ashamed of each other.
But he found someone else
Someone older than me
So all I can do is dream
Of what could have become
I lie in my bed
Wide awake thinking of him
With tears in my eyes
I really thought I'd found someone
But I was wrong
And now he's gone
So I just sit here dreaming
Of what could have become!

Alice Middleton (14)

TEENAGERS

T rends change
E verything gets on my nerves
E arly bedtimes - no more!
N ever stop moaning
A ge goes into double figures
G rumpy moods start
E ducation gets more interesting and challenging
R elatives say that you look just like your mum and dad
S pots!

Glenn Ashby (13)

MY MUM

She is big and bold
and getting old.
She loves and cares
and even shares.
Her smile is the sunshine,
her tears are the rain,
her anger is the thunder,
but she is very plain.
Her brown curly hair
hangs below her shoulders,
her big brown eyes are warming,
but when she has a temper
she loses it without warning.
She loves vodka and Coke
and especially blokes,
so that's my mum explained to you,
so can you imagine what I'm like too?

Emma White (14)

HERE I STAND BEFORE YOU

With little confidence I stand before you,
Colour of the mountains and dirt on this earth,
Wrapped up so delicately
Within thoughts of all the joy and misery.
From the past fifteen years of my life
Still I stand before you
Colour of the night,
With even less confidence than before.

Chantelle Louise Harrison (15)

JUBILEE

To celebrate the jubilee
Lots of people marching
Down the mall

Joy and hope
Love and peace
Are people's thoughts

A time to think
What has been
Over fifty years

Friends and family
Partners and neighbours
All as one

Marching, marching
Flags are flying
As we walk

Concorde flying
Up above
As a symbol

Many memories
In the air
To remember

The day is over
People tired
Back to bed.

Martin Ash (13)

WHAT IS A TEENAGER?

What is a teenager?
Does it start when you hit thirteen
Or when you start your adolescences?
Is it backchatting your parents
Or controlling the TV?
Is it all about boys and girls
Or just about you?
Is about staying up late
Or being the best dancer at a disco?
Is it about when you first start a fight
Or when you have a pop idol on TV?
Is it about what you wear
Or how you act at school?
Is it about what you eat
Or how loud you yell at your brother or sister?
Is it about how many people you've been out with
Or how many you will go out with?
Is it about being rich
Or what music you like?
Is it about how clever you are
Or how people see you?
No!
I'll tell you what being a teenager is all about,
Being you inside and out,
Being proud of what you've become,
And looking to the future for what you'll be,
So think for one second,
How many of us are teenagers now . . .

Sophie Smith (13)

FEELINGS OF A SOUL

I'm standing in the middle
Of a big black gaping hole,
It really is a riddle
As it's eating through my soul.

My heart feels really grey,
My body's full of aches and pains,
I haven't got any say
As in my soul I feel it rains.

As my spirit gets so weak
And my body becomes ill,
I really cannot peak
So I need a special pill.

My mind says do me harm
And I really cannot say
Why I cannot remain calm
So I think that I must pray.

My shoulders I must shrug
Until I reach the crest
I really need a hug
So that I can overcome the test.

Katie Hutton (13)

THE ISLAND

The azure ocean surrounded a dwarf island
Bright yellow sand sparkled
Pine trees swayed from side to side
And welcomed us with open arms.

Gum leaking out of tropical trees
Hard rock piled so neatly
And fountains of waterfalls,
Welcomed us with open arms.

An arid canyon
A sweet smell
The burning sun
Welcomed us with open arms.

Oh island so unknown,
Oh island so down low,
Why do you welcome us with open arms?

Punam Vyas (13)

HALLOWE'EN NIGHT

Darkness is falling,
The hour is at hand,
Monsters and ghouls,
Wander the land!

Witches coming calling,
Flying through the air,
Beware of the vampires,
Go out if you dare!

The dead shall walk the earth tonight,
They could be lurking out of sight,
Around dark corners they will wait,
To gather souls is their fate.

Gather your sweets; don't dawdle,
Rush home,
Remember don't stay for too long
On your own.

Midnight had come,
Be prepared to scream,
It's here again
Have a good Hallowe'en.

Natasha Cantelo (13)

WHEN YOU'RE A TEENAGER

You listen to radical lyrics
That inspire and provoke
Causing perturbation, fever and commotion
Have feeling, indispensable intention and proclaim true motives
That the world's too blind to see.

You dream, hope and love for the unobtainable fortunes
Desire new opportunities, choices
Nourish upon new ideas, encouraged and fed by our peers
And sharply you focus upon the target
Which introduces us to the gates of our palace.

Under pressure we fragment
As forces drive from every direction
They blast and gain impact as the pressure increases till we crumble
Exams hall are irritable
They increase the feeble fall while the drastic weight intensifies

When the catwalks open
Are you true of counterfeit
The spotlight lands, mask falls
Your brand new outfit simply fizzles out
As the peacock brigade stride by

We're strong enough to construct our foundations
Although flaws in us you may find
As fragile as our structure may seem we lay upon it
Occasionally the odd brick falls
But we mutate our house from time to time until we reach the end.

Chantelle Goldsworthy (15)

CHARACTERS IN THE SOAPS

A shley Peacock has a squeaky voice,
B etty Eggleton is the village gossip.
C hloe Atkinson is dating one of the nicest guys on the block.
D rew Kirk has a bouncing baby,
E mma Watts has a baby as sweet as a cherry.
F elicity Scully has been a naughty girl,
G eena Gregory is the street's pearl.
H arold Bishop gets nicknamed by Lou 'Jelly Belly',
I an Beale's pickled onions at the chippy quiver like a
                                        bowlful of jelly.
J amie Mitchell from EastEnders is the cutest guy in soap,
K arl Kennedy is the best grandfather for baby Ben, or so he hopes!
L isa Fowler has a baby called Louise and is married to Mark,
M aureen Morgan won best actress at this year's Soap Awards, hark!
N orris Cole eavesdrops and gossips all the time,
O llie Reynolds has a boyfriend as zesty as lime.
P eggy Mitchell thinks she's the best landlady at the Queen Vic,
Q uivering Barry Evan's constantly has me in stitches.
R obert Sugden's attention is quite rare,
S onia Jackson is one of the friendliest girls on the square.
T oadfish Rebecchi has been on Ramsay Street for ages,
U ndoubtably, Libby Kennedy-Kirk is one of my favourite actresses.
V era Duckworth works at the café,
W ars in soaps always have explosive endings.
X mas in the soaps is always a disaster,
Y apping dogs are a must.
Z oe Slater's mother is Kat and to me they both sparkle like the stars!

Hannah Slesser (14)

OAP

He is as ancient as a caveman
Small an' flabby,
His hair is as white as snow
Grubby and bitter,
His head is as big as a football ready to kick
Astronomical and globe-shaped,
He is as bent as a stick
Over-grown and anorexic,
His nose is like an over-grown pig
Long and bulky,
His eyes are as blue as the sea,
Bright and clean,
His mouth is as huge as a cave
Immeasurable and dark,
His ears are as capacious as a over-grown tree
Colossal and ring-shaped,
His legs are as thin as twigs ready to break,
Bony and small.

Michelle Carey (13)

GRANDAD

Waiting for the phone to ring
For bad news to be said
When we are asleep in bed
Our grandad is in hospital
On his dying bed
Mum comes in early in the morning
And tells me he's passed away
I started to cry
As I didn't get to say goodbye.

Patricia Harper (13)

ROCK STAR

No longer a daydream
This is reality
Your room is wrecked
And so is your life
Breathe in some smoke
A handgun in your hand
Posters littered on the walls
Of your rock 'n' roll idols
They meant so much at the start
But they're now empty
Just vacant eyes
Boring through your skull
Leaving your mind dead
Blood drips onto the floor
From your latest cut
Black clouds swirl through your head
Leaving you with nightmares
Where did you go wrong?
On the long path you took
You loved the roar of the audience
The bang of the drums
The screech of the guitar
You never knew anything
From within your adolescence
Never felt sadness
Or neglect
Your hand still holds your gun
Which you lift to your head
Time to draw the final curtain over.

Taliesin Williams (13)

PIZZA

I wish life was like a pizza
It would please me to the brim
I would sit all day and eat it
Until I were no longer thin

If life was like a pizza
It would be o' so tasty
There would be so much to choose from
You wouldn't want to waste me

If life was like a pizza
The crispy bits would start
The juicy bits would end
And the tomatoes would be the heart

If life was like a pizza
What a happy life we'd have
We'd go into people's mouth holes
And shoot out into the lav!

We'd finish up in a river somewhere
We'd die amongst the fish
We'd blend into the countryside
And no longer be a tasty dish.

Sarah Whitaker (14)

MY STRANGE DAYS

Sometimes I'm happy after seeing my friends
Sometimes my head twists and bends
This is usually when I've had a school day
Where's there's been all work and no play.

Sometimes I try to calm down and relax
Sometimes it helps when my music's on at the max
This is usually to recover from a day
I wish I could have spent under the duvet.

Sometimes I feel happy and fine
Sometimes I can't stop laughing for saying a line
This is usually when I've had a strange day
And I wish the others could also be as cheery as May.

Emma Stobbs (13)

A To Z Of Poetry

A   is for apple that's rosy and red,
B   is for bear, which I hug in my bed.
C   is for clothes that I wear every day,
D   is for dog with which I love to play.
E   is for elephant that's big and fat,
F   is for funny things that I laugh at.
G   is for golden, the colour the sun shines,
H   is for headache that I get sometimes.
I   is for Indian that lives in the forest,
J   is for Jasmine that I get from the florist.
K   is for kangaroo that jumps so high,
L   is the light shining from the sky.
M   is my mum, who I love so much,
N   are my neighbours, with whom I keep in touch.
O   is the opposition, who I have to win,
P   is for pyjamas that we sleep in.
Q   is for quiet, the sound of silence,
R   is for resistance from all the violence.
S   is the sweetness of all birds' song,
T   is tranquillity, for which we long.
U   is for unhappy when we make a mistake,
V   is for value of the friends that we make.
W   is for wisdom, which I see in you,
X   is for X-ray so we can see through.
Y   is for youth, when we are so able,
Z   is for Zimmer frame, when we are unstable.

Joanne Goffin (14)

GOING OUT

All the dresses are laying about,
Her hand hovers over them, indecisively.
Finally she picks one out.
The short red dress fits her perfectly.

The tiny silver hearts
Are chosen to adorn her ears.
She clips on the tiny back parts
Each heart is a shimmering silver tear.

The red lip liner is applied,
It ran over her lip
Then she smiled
As she replaced the sharpened tip.

Dark eyeliner under her eyes
Coffee coloured eye shadow above,
With mascara her eyelashes curl and rise
And she tints her cheeks with a soft powder puff.

With the black straps tied tightly
On her black high-heeled shoes,
She leaves the house to catch her ride,
Like a China doll, as she moves.

Laura Williams (14)

A TYPICAL SCHOOL DAY

Every Monday morning is the same,
The school bell rings again,
Teachers sing children's names,
While they answer with a scream.

While maths work is completed,
English is deleted,
Whereas French is tolerated,
Science is invigorated,

Lunchtime is an enjoyment,
Dinner ladies are an annoyance,
School meals are a disappointment,
Playing is anticipated.

After the final bell,
Children rush to the well,
Where their parents, who they tell,
Have been waiting for a while.

Louise Nesbitt (14)

A LADDER IS BORN

To each person a ladder is born
Each step to represent your next path
Every path made with different choices
Either ending in tears or you'll be able to laugh

Don't take advantage that to each step grows another
If you take the wrong step your ladder could fall
Treat it as a mistake and a chance to start afresh
Goals take time to reach, but succeed and you'll stand tall

Once you reach your target, don't just stop there
It's not then all over and come to an end
You can't just give up the moment you succeed
Build upon all, your ladder will always extend

Don't ever feel your hand cannot be held
No one's ever far enough away that you can't reach
You're never expected to gain all on your own
Everyone has experiences they are willing to teach

Every opportunity given to you, always take it
And never forget, your ladder is what you make it.

Shelley Flaherty (15)

LIFE

What *is* the meaning of life?
A commonly asked question
A commonly unanswered question

In this world, you see things you don't want to,
But, do we really have a choice?
The world controls itself, you control what happens in it

You will never know the reason for us being here
But take advantage of what you've got
You never know, tomorrow you may not have it

It will all end some day
But, how far will we get?
Will we ever fly to Pluto and live there?

Just think, you could be in a dream right now
And you wouldn't know about it
You could be in a computer game, being controlled by someone else

A question never going to be answered
A question always going to be asked
What *is* the meaning of life?

Niall Clark (14)

GROWING UP

Greasy hair,
Spotty skin,
Mood swings,
Isn't growing up a pain!

New schools,
New friends,
More responsibility,
Boyfriends and girlfriends,
Isn't growing up exciting!

Nagging parents,
Babysitting,
Shouting and arguing,
'Where have you been and who with?'
Isn't growing up a bore!

Starting school,
Making friends,
Little birthday tea parties,
Trips to the park,
Playing with Barbies,
Isn't being little cool!

Jennifer Lorimer (13)

THE WAITING GAME

Hours I've been waiting
Well it seems like that to me.
I got that call at two o'clock
And now it's a quarter-past three.
He said he'd be right over
Was he lying to me?

I got that call at two o'clock
And now it's way past three!
It's coming up to six o'clock
And I've been waiting for hours.

I'm not a happy bunny,
I want my happy hours.
I'll have to wait I suppose
Until way after six
For my dealer friend
To bring my special fix.

Chocolate, chips and candy sticks.

Alice Cross (13)

SUMMER NIGHTS

I love the summer months,
With the sapphire blue nights.
I gaze through my window
And the sparkling silver moon gleams through,
With a soft gentle breeze cooling me.

During the night I peacefully sleep,
While the birds outside are chirping.
The smell of a barbecue drifts by my window
And the echoing sounds of laughter can be heard.

As morning draws closer,
With the sunlight beaming through,
I shuffle and stir,
As a new day breaks through.

Sarah Richards (14)

ARRGH!

Whatever I do is wrong.
Arrgh!
If I try to help I just get shouted at.
Arrgh!
When I don't help I get shouted at.
Arrgh!
Life isn't fair.
Arrgh!
I can't say anything right.
Arrgh!
Whatever I do isn't good enough.
Arrgh!
Nobody understands.
Arrgh!

Michael Dodds (13)

IS IT GREAT OR DO I HATE!

Being a teenager
is really scary,
Cos you're growing up
and going hairy.

Hormones are changing
going up and down,
Making your head
spin round and round.

It has its good points and
then its bad,
Cos once you're happy
you'll soon get sad.

Having parties and
going wild,
Always remembering you're
still a child.

Being careful
is the key,
Keep yourself safe
and then you'll see.

What it is like
to be your mum,
Is it cool
or is it glum?

Play it safe
and you'll be okay,
To see it through
the rest of your days.

Charlene Bundy (13)

LIVES OF NEGATIVITY

Nowadays, violence seems to empower the young souls of today and
tomorrow, causing their lives to go extremely sour.

Nowadays, AIDS and that destroying lives, in order to survive they
have the urge to borrow.

Sorrow, sorrow, sorrow is now the moral of our days, and this is the
outcome in which it pays, through our iniquitous ways.

Nowadays, groupies, the Mafia and gangsters are never ever pranksters,
killing and destroying lives to revive their lives with negativity
and money.
It's an addiction
Never ever showing, portraying consideration.

Money, money, money is now becoming the epicentre of the world's
contradictory tremor.

We need to start to respect, instead of neglect
Soon enough negativity will eject
Out of our planet.

What this world needs is love, peace, joy and unity,
Soon enough this world will be walking together accordingly.

Just wait and see!

Joshua Okungbaiye (14)

SOUL

My soul is deeper than the ocean
And bluer than the sky,
Appearing simple is its illusion
But it's more complicated than my mind.

It is as quiet as the wind
But stronger than a gale,
It guides my life with ease
Without it I would fail.

Louisa Smyllie (15)

THE RHYTHM OF LIFE

When you are a child
Starting very small
It's hard to think that you'll be tall at all
And the pain of growing inches
Is just a little of the pain to come
For slipping into the rhythm of life has only just begun
As you get a little older
You start to feel the beat
Which to your surprise everybody's tapping their feet
You don't know why yet
And if you'll do it too
All you know is the beat is tricky and hard
And the steps are moving too fast
As time passes and you do too
You start to realise you can tap your foot too
Then you look more closely at the rhythm of life
And see
That the taps of all the feet are different
And yours are too
Some of the taps go together and some don't
So whoever you may be in life
The rhythm is still playing along
For people may pass
Children may laugh
But hey, the rhythm of life is still moving.

Rose Black (13)

MY FUTURE

Ever since I was little,
I have wanted to become a doctor.
Ever since I was little,
I have wanted to make a difference.
Ever since I was little,
I was afraid of not achieving my goals.

Ever since I was little,
I knew I would have to work really hard.
Ever since I was little,
I was scared that I would not make the grades.
Ever since I was little,
It was all in the very distant future.

Just from this moment,
I realise it is time to decide my future.
Just from this moment,
I have to prove myself to everyone.
Just from this moment,
I am terrified.

Rebecca Fletcher (14)

TEENAGERS

T   eenagers always like to chill out
E   ngineering takes the lad's fancy, no doubt
E   nergy is at an all time height
N   othing beats a good old party night
A   ll the girls love their make-up and hair
G   roovy clothes are what we like to wear
E   very weekend and holidays we cheer, *'No school!'*
R   eally, we teenagers are *'Oh so cool!'*

Richard Brickhill (13)

A Sad Way To Love

At first I thought our love was meant to be, it was fate
Although soon the love in my heart grew to hate
You hurt me in every possible way
Yet I still tried to love you for one more day
So hard did I try and try
Finally, I just died inside
No more could I cope or carry on
No longer did my heart sing a song
No getting back together, one last time
Right now you've finally crossed the line
Never shall I love you like I did before
Even if my heart and soul are sore
I just can't take this hurt any more
For the longest time you drove me insane
Now, never will I take you back again.

Natasha McCready (14)

Insurrection

The questions that echo through the sound
All fall on deaf ears,
And the search for the revolution
Has been lost in the desert, for years.

And all the while, the vicious sleep,
We are left to contemplate
Why the world divides,
And neither side appreciates,

A separation that without causes war,
And yet with, war still rages free.
And the need for constant power
Overpowers us constantly.

Lianne Clark (15)

PERFECTION

Perfection is an art
Sought by the heart
Or maybe it's the head
That searches instead
For the thought deep inside
That everything is okay.
Not for tomorrow
But just for today
Everyone searches
But not all find
You'll see it there somewhere
In everyone's mind
They want to be perfect
They want to be best
But really we're all
Just as good as the rest.

Amma Brefo (14)

THE RESPONSIBILITY OF GETTING OLDER

Responsibility is high, responsibility is huge.
It's a great constant pain in your head.
It's there from when you wake
Until when you go to sleep.

As you get older, it grows stronger
You have to do this
You can't do that.

There's no messing about
Like when you were a kid.

Kanisha Jacobs (14)

NEW SCHOOL

When I started my new school, new friends were hard to find,
Nobody wanted to know me, but I didn't mind.
My old friends who still liked me, were at a new school.
Whilst I sat on my own, eating lunch in the hall.
As days flew by, no friends were in sight,
What was wrong with me?
Why wasn't I liked?
That was until I found a new friend.
I was so happy, now all my problems would end,
I spent the remaining schooldays as happy as can be.
Will I get more friends? I'll just wait and see.

At the end of the year, my gang began to grow,
Now next year my friends and I will be raring to go!

Kayleigh Thomas (14)

I SEE DARKNESS

I see darkness everywhere
In every corner and every nook
And shadows pass right by me
Ignoring me - as if I didn't exist.
I feel a cold tingling
Course through my entire body
And the need for understanding
Filling my head.
I'm confused and dazed
My vision is blurred
Figures swirl around
And now it dawns on me
Like the first glimpse of the sun
This is what it feel like
To be dead.

Bryony Betts (13)

MESSY ROOM

My room, my room
It's such a mess
Here's my shoes
There's my dress.

Dad has given up
Mum can't stand it
But I'll clean it
Starting bit by bit.

Where should I begin?
I'm totally confused
Never mind my brother's mess
I'm the one accused.

My brother's room is a mess
But who would care?
No one says a word
Life just isn't fair.

I'll clean it today
But it'll happen again
The same old thing
And everyone insane!

Jharna Bhatia (14)

THE CREW AT NUMBER 28

My grandma is called Lillian,
She's very nice and kind.
She only lives next door
So she's not very hard to find.

My grandad is called Tom,
He lives next door as well.
He likes playing on the organ,
But he loves me more, you can tell.

They've got a dog called Meg
A springer spaniel, brown and white.
When she's let off the lead
She flies off, just like a kite.

So that's the crew next door
They're not such a bad bunch.
I'll have to go now anyway,
I'm having bacon and egg for lunch.

Kelly Woodward (13)

LIVE YOUR DREAMS

There is no pain,
There are battle scars . . .

        There is no shame,
        There is pride . . .

There are no fools,
But there is dignity . . .

        There are no idiots,
        There are darers . . .

There is no love,
There is respect . . .

        There is no impossible,
        Only the possible . . .

There is no stupidity,
There are geniuses . . .

        There is no fear . . .
        There are no regrets . . .

Live your dreams.

Guy Tarbuck (13)

IT'S A FREE COUNTRY, RIGHT?

I wake up in the morning
In my comfy bed

I wake up in the morning,
Wishing I was dead.

I pull on my clothes
Thinking about the day ahead

I beg for money
Whilst I pack up my bed.

I go to school and
Meet my mate

A homeless life,
One I really hate.

The bell is ringing,
It's time to eat

I am freezing,
Stopping every stranger I meet.

It's three o'clock
I say goodbye

It's three o'clock,
I wonder why?

I am walking home,
I see a man against a wall

I look up
I see a boy who has it all.

Stephen Rocks (14)

MASK

I stand on the top of my hill
And wear my mask upon my face,
I prepare for my descent
It won't be easy -
But everyone has a hill
And the sad truth is, that everyone wears a mask to walk down it in.

Alas! If only people could have their own faces showing,
Then I'm sure that the land of hills would be so much happier.

Nevertheless, down I go.
I have no map.
All I know is the direction in which I am going,
Down!

Which way the path will turn, I have no clue,
What obstructions may delay or divert me
I'll just have to wait and see.

It's worth my while, for I know that when I reach the bottom
I will receive my reward:
There is the chance to unmask my face
And look in a mirror.

I'm there now
My reward I seek,
But now I take my mask off.
I'm sad and alone
I see what the reflection has to offer.
Not a face, but *Rest In Peace* upon a stone.

Josh Goodman (13)

MY WORLD

I used to stand there and just stare
I used to see things that weren't there,
It wasn't reality
I didn't care.

I could just stand there and would tend
To think up things that would blend
With the way I would like the world to be.
In that world now
I cannot see.

I think of the mind as a sink
You can pull the plug on what you think.

Now I stand there and just stare
And see *my* world
Just stripped bare.

I can stand there with my eyes shut,
But the connection to *my* world is finely cut.

On the subject, I reflect
On all the things I should have kept.

Alexander Bernas (13)

THE HAWK

Sitting watching from my window
I see it glide in the sky
Watching its prey with its vicious eye
Slowly it turns and fairly fast
It swoops down, grabbing the starling from the grass.
A flurry of feathers is all that is seen
As the bird with clutched claws, flies over the green.

Jacqui Crowe (14)

GOING OUT

Home from school,
Lock the door
Before I go out
Just five hours more.

Have a shower,
Wash my hair.
Shave my legs
But take great care.

Pick out an outfit,
Gotta look good.
Classiest gal
In the neighbourhood!

Eyeliner, lip gloss,
Eye shadow too.
Nearly done now
One last thing to do.

Paint my nails
Add bangles and rings.
The right hairstyle
Is the most important thing.

I'm at the club now,
Walk in the door.
Grab a man
And hit the floor!

Jenny Leigh (13)

CLEAN YOUR ROOM!

'Clean your room,
Clean your room,
Here's a duster
And a broom'

'Eat your food,
Eat your food,
Don't put Mother
In a mood'

'Walk your dog,
Walk your dog,
Or I'll turn it
Into a frog'

'Go to bed,
Go to bed,
Or I'll lock you
In the shed'

'All this stuff
In one day
Until it is
The first of May!'

Kimberley Spence (13)

MUSIC IS MY REFUGE

Music is my refuge,
Flow into my ears, and drown my brain
Events on the outside can pause,
Rewind, press play and hear it again.

Listen to the lyrics,
Why not bathe in every single word?
Take them in and digest
Acknowledge all the things you've heard.

Music is my refuge,
I visit it almost every day.
Events on the outside can pause,
Pick your track, and then press play.

Jemila Elahcene (14)

MY ROOM

When I walk into my room
I see darkness, hardness, coldness and sadness.
When I step into my room
I have to jump onto the bed -
There's so much clutter about.

When I stand in my room
The posters all cry.
When I'm quiet in my room,
I hear the crying -
It's the people who died there before.

When I look out of the window in my room, they disappear.
They are replaced by steel bars.
When I go to open the door in my room
It will not turn.
It's locked, there is no way out.

When I try to sleep in my room
I hear the baby screaming -
The one who will never leave.

The description of my room is like
The description of someone's life.
But does it sound like *yours?*

Dominique Homer (15)

THE VIEW FROM ONE OF MANY

Trapped within your own world,
Pushed into believing you're nothing.
Kicked against the wall with insults,
Feeling only the pain of trusting.

From once a carefree time,
To the miserable pain of appearance,
A life of mixed confusion
And only you can feel the difference.

Laughed at, joked about,
It's not always how they see it.
You are who you are,
And they'd better try believing it.

There is the good and the bad,
But sometimes it's as if you're unseen.
So I hope you know what it is
To be living the life of a teen.

Ellen Matkins (13)

HOW LONG?

How long will flowers stand?
How long will birds fly?
How long will cats miaow?
How long will dogs bark?
How long will horses gallop?
How long will humans last?
How long will Earth last?
How long is time?
These we do not know, but
yet we know length is time!

Helen Stott (13)

MY NIECE SAMMY

My little niece called Sammy
She has a wobbly head
She crawls across the floor
And even falls off the bed!
As soon as Dad comes in the room
She laughs, she giggles, she smiles
But if she's in a nasty mood
She'll cry just for a while.
When she's eating all her food
She makes a funny sound
But then she takes a great big bite
And gulps it all right down!
I have a niece called Sammy
She's nine months old; quite young,
When she comes into my house
She's always lots of fun.
My little niece called Sammy
She's got a sleepyhead
She's getting very tired
So I'll tuck her into bed.

Sarah Robinson (13)

FIREWORKS

F   ireworks are noisy and colourful
I   love all of the bright colours
R   eds, oranges, pinks and greens
E   ven blues, purples and yellows.
W   hy do they make such a noise?
O   thers even hear them from inside
R   emember, remember the 5th of November
K   eep safe and stand well back
S   parklers are fun, but dangerous too!

Linzi Morrison (13)

THE FUNERAL OF LOVE

Life was such a beautiful song,
Now something is missing, that's right, you're gone!
I wish I could say it was meant to be,
But it's my heart that can't set you free.

It has come to me as a bit of a shock,
Like frying something in a wok.
The way I remember you is like a warm sunset,
It rises when you least expect.
Now you're cold and completely dead
I won't forget you, not in my head.

The funeral was perfect as funerals go,
I wept with sorrow, as I let you go.
Your mother was there, she had tears in her eyes
She said to me softly, 'It was a bit of a surprise.'

I'll never forget you, but I have to move on,
As many things go, I'll be moving quite slow.
With relatives behind me and Count Paris back
I hope you'll forgive me, if I pack.

I'll be loving you forever, I'll visit your grave,
You were my saviour
So bold-hearted and brave.
One day we will be back together, just wait and see.
Remember I am *Juliet*, the only girl you need.

Fatimah Ayoade (14)

MONSTER IN THE BIN

Sleepy time for Ella
Mummy tucks her in.
But Ella doesn't like sleepy time . . .
Because there's a monster in the bin!

Ella wakes up crying
Mummy doesn't hear.
She knows that something scary . . .
Is hiding very near!

Ella looks around her,
Some scary monsters come.
Ella doesn't like them . . .
So she cries loudly for her mum!

Ella cries out loudly,
But Mummy stays in bed.
Ella sees some pictures . . .
But they are in here head.

Ella cries her loudest,
This time Mummy hears.
Mummy cuddles Ella . . .
And wipes away her tears!

Ella now likes sleepy time,
Because Mummy bought a light.
She turns it on at sleepy time . . .
And it shines all through the night!

Charlotte Driver (13)

SCHOOL

Everyone hates to go to school,
It's really, really boring.
Some teachers just go on and on,
We nearly end up snoring.

Out of bed, right on time,
No way I can dawdle
Mum's making my favourite breakfast,
Toast and eggs with noodles.

I'm dashing to catch the bus,
Mum says she wants a goodbye cuddle,
Please Mum, please hurry up
Or you'll get me into trouble.

As I walk up to the gates,
The whole day is dawning,
Perhaps the pet rat in science has died,
We could go into mourning.

The school day has begun,
No joke to tell or laughing to do.
Teachers are continually talking
The pupils have not got a clue.

It's great for all my friends and I,
We're having an hour for lunch,
Now's the time to have lots of fun
We're eating sweets called 'Cherries Crunch'.

Back to lessons to get bored again,
It's like the Devil's Hell,
A cheer of happiness spreads around,
We have heard the end of school bell.

Tina Mason (13)

I AM
(A poem of friendship)

I am the wings
That help you to fly
And all through your life
You'll soar in the sky.
I am the soft breeze
That whispers in your ear,
'I am your strength
And I'll always be here.'
I am the sunshine
That brightens up your day.
I am the captor
I will chase your fears away.
I am your angel
I watch from up above.
I'll guide you and protect you
With my everlasting love.
I am the arms which cradle you
When you cannot sleep.
I am the love which in your heart
You'll always want to keep.
I am that summer scent
That lingers all day long.
I am the bird up in my tree
Singing my beautiful song.
I am almost anything
But most of all your friend
And no matter what life throws at me,
I'll be there until the end.

Clare Hickman (15)

THE LADY

As she stood in the wind
Her black hair swayed to and fro
She danced about in circles in the moonlight
Her cheeks aglow
Her long cloak glistened amongst the stars

The dawn has broken, a new day is here
The sunrise can be seen from miles away
The sky is so blue and clear
She skips into the yellow cornfields and twirls around
So lost in excitement, she can't hear a sound

In the heat of the red sun, her brow does glow
She walks slowly through the green grass
Knowing it's time to go

The lady is tall, pretty and brown
She is always happy and never wears a frown
Her name is Lolita
And I'm sure you'd like to meet her?

Stephanie Anderson (13)

A DAY AT THE RACES

The clock struck ten on the day of the races,
It's time to go as I tie my laces.
I need so much money to place on the Tote
Whilst the favourite in the first, gets my vote.

We finally arrive for the meeting at noon,
Excited and ready, not a moment too soon.
We take our place at the back of the stands,
Whilst over the other side of the course
A helicopter lands.

Inside the paddock, horses and jockeys
Begin to parade,
Some of them small, but others well made.
The horses are now on their way to the start,
As the commentator shouts the horse called Playapart.

As the starter pulls the lever,
The horse in stall five, throws Jason Weaver.
What a great experience this day has been,
For me to witness this excellent scene.

Richard Bainbridge (13)

SUICIDE NOTE

The most beautiful thing I ever wrote
Was my suicide note.
I told my parents I hated them, my brother too,
And how taking my life was the best thing I'd do.
I told my only friend,
It wasn't her fault, it had to end.
I told him I loved him, and always had,
It wasn't his fault my life was bad.
Sue my school if you feel the need,
They always knew, yet took no heed,
Don't keep my things, nor give them away,
Burn the lot, without delay.
Please don't cry,
I was always going to die,
I just had the brain,
To do it now, quick with no pain.
I'd like red roses on my grave,
And the inscription to say 'She was brave.'
Then I slit my wrists, must have done it wrong,
Woke up in hospital, hope I don't stay long.

Charlotte Cameron (14)

LOVE

Love can bring you together,
Love can break you apart.
Love can turn you head over heels
Love can break your heart.

Love is a term used all too often,
It's lost its special touch.
But you'll always know when you've found the one,
Because you'll cherish them so, so much.

'Luv' is sent in text messages
'Love' is written in a card.
But when you lose the one you love,
The word 'love' seems very hard.

You tell your family you love them,
You tell your friends this too.
But how do you know that the truth is told,
When someone says, 'I love you'?

If you've found the one you love
And you let your feelings flow.
You'll realise that loving means -
To love, but let them go.

Vikki Champion (14)

LIFE

Moonlight shines through the window,
I'm lying on my bed
But I can't get to sleep,
With so many thoughts in my head.

Hopes and wishes flash through my mind,
Anything's possible it seems,
Then worries from my life
Put a hold on all of my dreams.

School, boys, friends and family,
My mind's in overload,
My life is all mixed up
If only my feelings slowed.

Life's a roller coaster
Sometimes you're up and sometimes you're down,
Life can make you smile
And life can make you frown.

Siobhan Gilliam (13)

WEBSTER

*(Webster was my Pyrenean mountain dog
and on the 13th July he had to be put to sleep.
I have written this poem in his memory.)*

He had white fluffy hair
And a *big* black nose,
He looked like a polar bear
He would sit down and pose.

He had *big* round eyes
He was covered in drool,
He was an enormous size
He was very cool.

He was my best friend,
He was only seven.
When he sadly got sick
And went to doggy heaven.

He was the best,
Now we are apart.
He is at rest
He will always have
A special place in my heart.

Jamie Danks (13)

No Cloud Has A Silver Lining For Me

The world had crushed my hopes years ago
The world is too heavy for my shoulders
My mind is filled with sorrow
Grief and agony caused by other people
These feelings keep repeating in my mind.

My feelings lead me blindly into the darkness
Which path is right for me?
Will I aspire to wealth and great fortune
Or will I live in vain?
Will I trust people and be exploited
Or will I trust no one, not even myself?

The depraved feelings lay within
They struggle to break out
Should I surrender and let them win?
Fighting them seems meaningless.

Every choice I make I am lost
The world changes too fast
I try my best
But whatever I do, I fail.

Every second the end of the tunnel draws nearer
My unbound soul has been restrained
My mind is slowly sinking into silence
I cling on to the last grains of life
But they keep slipping through my fingers.

Arjan Verdi (13)

WHO WE ARE

If I were a soldier
Would anyone cry for me?
If I were a rock star
Would anyone cheer for me?
If I were a victim
Would anyone stick up for me?
But half the days, the wind is blowing
Erasing memories.

We're the rise and fall
Of this year's century.
We take it in our stride
To kill our enemies.
What if
We turned our backs
Just like we always do,
And finish off the pain
We know we all can do.

If I were a killer
Would anyone care for me?
If I were a child abuser
Would anyone rescue me?
If I were a rapist
Would anyone forgive me?
If I were a normal child
Would anyone listen to me?

Rebecca Stone (14)

THE VAST UNEXPLORED CORNERS
OF THE DARK UNIVERSE

The arms of the universe swept out and in, with the ferocity of
all of Neptune's oceans.
Like it was possessed.
Troubled, the weight of the world weighing upon its fragile shoulders.
It was as though the tide was coming back and forth,
in a variety of motions.
The pale frail face looking out, solemn weary eyes gave a glance of fear
A face of wrinkles, a mouth closed and tight.
Nothing in his powers he could do, not even if he tried
with all his might.
The world crashing down, peace no longer.
War, crime, hunger.
Secret mysteries being unfolded, the hope of peace grows fonder.
Why can't we live and let live?

Katrina Sturrock (14)

WHAT THE OTHERS THINK!

What clothes to wear
What boys to date,
Who to love
And who to hate.

What food to eat,
What drink to drink,
What phone to have
What will they think!

Does it matter what they say?
. . . Yes!

Danielle Galpin (13)

I HAD A DREAM

I had a dream of ending world hunger,
To make people live much longer,
To see how their future lives would change.
I had a dream of ending world wars
And changing them to world peace.
As for me that would never be
Unless we stick our heads together
And think of a solution to make things better.
I had a dream to end racism,
And make people come together as one.
Like the moon, Earth and sun.
We're not on this Earth to be horrible and cruel.
We were put here to help each other
We are here to stick together for one another.
The only thing I can say is I had a dream -
                              But not anymore!

Salumé Van-Tankeren (13)

FRUSTRATION

The way the anger brews inside
This anger has nowhere to hide
So when at last you've had enough and push it all aside
The anger gets you first and rises like the tide
Your face goes red and you go mad
Sometimes this can make you sad
The time in which this process takes, at least ten seconds,
Depending on your state
But whoever it is who upsets you, just walk away,
Don't let them decide your fate
Just remember the person you are on the inside
And remember you're great!

James Atkins (13)

LOVE

Love is the deepest emotion,
Full of joy and sorrow,
Digging deep into our hearts,
Mixing up our feelings.
Tongue-tied and in a dream,
We set the world to right.

Love comes in many ways,
The love to our family
And friends.
The love from a girl to a boy
And a boy to a girl.
Love is more than friendship,
Love is trust.

Love can be confusing and disorientating,
But what is life without love,
And the support from our families
To help us through these difficult years?
Love is what helps us through the good and bad.
Love gives us hope,
Love is priceless.

Kay Taylor (14)

INSIDE MY HEAD

Inside my head there's a swirling mist,
Dark and unknowing,
Longing to break out
And reveal its many secrets.

Inside my head, there's a swirling mist,
Worrying about exams.
Wondering what people will say
Deciding not to care.

Inside my head there's a swirling mist,
Encouraging my friends,
Urging us to embrace the depth
Of our turning world.

Inside my head there's a swirling mist,
Slowly revolving around,
Beginning to make sense
Turning darkness to light.

Natalie Pressick (13)

WHAT IS THE FUTURE?

The future is you
The future is me
The future is everyone you can see

The future is you
The future is I
To follow our dreams and touch the sky

The future is them
The future is us
To work as a team, with care and trust

The future is children
The future is teens
To push yourself to accomplish your dreams

The future is living
The future is not dead
If you have the courage to hold up your head

The future is you
The future is I
We can follow our dreams and touch the sky.

Olivia Doran (13)

HAIL

I'm hard and I'm violent
I make children wail,
I come down on you
Like a pint or a pail.
I'm damp but vicious
I ruin your mail.
I'm no good to you
When you're using a sail.
I can easily break things
Many precious, like snails.
I'm strong, you're weak,
I hurt you, you wail.
You've probably guessed it,
Yep! I'm hail.

Laura Stewart (13)

WHY ME?

It's funny how,
I'm all alone now,
No one can hear my cry,
All the people just go and walk on
and pass me by.
Why can't they see how much I'm hurting
deep inside?
They treat me like I'm not there,
like I've just gone and died.
All I want is for them to listen to me,
If they don't, my emotions, they'll never see,
I really want to be someone,
But it's hard when all my loved ones
are gone.

Katrina Struthers (13)

WHAT WE HAVE MADE THE WORLD

The world seems like a peaceful place
Yet we live in fear,
That war, disease and soldiers
Will come and find us here

We think we lead a tranquil life
But we are unaware
Of those unlucky places
And what is happening there

War is all around us
And we say that we feel safe
But day-by-day we wonder
When death will snatch us from this place

We say we live in harmony
But really we do not,
We don't have time to stop and think
About the problems we have got

There is no rest or stillness
No pause for thought in our world
Nobody stops and thinks awhile
Before the insults are hurled

They find no time to stop and wait
And hear the deathly silence
They won't pause to negotiate
Before they begin the violence

We make the world an unfair place
And blame everyone else
When the thing we should be doing
Is to blame ourselves.

Hannah Charnley (13)

BETTER A JUNKIE THAN A SOLDIER

Better a junkie than a soldier,
Getting high on *coke* or *smack,*
Not fear-soaked, frenzied adrenaline.
Easier to live on the streets,
Than survive in blood-soaked trenches.
Track marks on your veins,
Not bullet-wounds in your flesh.
Simpler to sell yourself for fast money,
Than to sell your soul to your country.
Truer are crimes that fund addiction,
Than killing randomly on command.
Your only goal is another fix,
Not an empty victory.
It's easier to be tortured by your own need,
Than enslaved by the military.
Glassy eyes and a half-life,
Not shell-shocked trying to stay alive.
Better to die from an overdose
Than from pointless martyrdom.
Better a junkie than a soldier,
But either way,
You're dead and gone.

Dora Daniel (15)

IT DOESN'T MATTER

It doesn't matter what colour I am
Or the clothes I wear
You shouldn't mind if I wear glasses
Or the way I do my hair.

It doesn't matter if I'm pretty or not
Or if I come top in each subject.
You should take no notice whether I'm big or small,
So why do I feel like a reject?

It doesn't matter if I have a different accent,
I wish this would end,
For I am just a lonely girl,
In need of a friend.

Claire Rosser (13)

DREAM WORLD

I live in a world of peace and love,
Everyone's caring, like a gentle dove,
More and more every day,
Like birds of a feather together we stay
No pollution, no litter,
I find people aren't bitter,
Because in a world of peace and love
Everyone's caring like a gentle dove.

I live in a land which is very far,
From the terrible nightmare of world war.
Every one following the footsteps of law
No one is breaking the rules which I saw,
The grass so green
No one is mean
The sky so blue
There's loads to do
Because in a world of peace and love
Everyone's caring like a gentle dove.

In a world of peace and love,
Everyone's caring, like a gentle dove,
The world where I'm living no one can see,
That in my mind it's a dream for me.

Elissa Newton (13)

THE WORLD THROUGH MY EYES

The world as I see it
Is a pretty weird place
With all our different ways,
With all our different lives.

This world as I see it
With all its different cultures and religions.
We all harmonise together
Making this world a better place.

Throughout our lives
We go through many events
Which, without the support of friends and families
We could not cope with.

Even though some people dislike school,
It is there to help us
To help our future
For the sake of others and ourselves.

The future is destined to be a better place for all of us,
as we all know it.

And that is the world through my eyes.

Jenny Guan (13)

A FRIENDSHIP LOST

Spreading those lies, leaving me in tears,
You've been my friend for all these years.
I never knew there was so much spite,
Trouble is, I don't want to fight.

Angry thoughts rage through my head.
It's a scary feeling, one of dread.
I've never felt this way before
And I really don't want to anymore.

What did I do? What's really so bad?
I can't believe I'm feeling so sad.
The worst thing is, this roller coaster won't stop.
My only wish is to turn back the clock.

I thought friends were meant to be there,
Stay together whatever; always care.
Unfortunately this does not seem to be true
And I am left alone without you.

Jessie Jamieson (15)

TEENAGE FEELINGS

Teenagers are in the in-between
The growing the not quite there
Sometimes we're full of happiness
And sometimes it's just not fair.

The anger will build up inside
Until suddenly you just let rip
You go and speak to your parents
'Oh stop giving us all the lip.'

We feel we are the only ones
Which makes us sad and cry
It's like no one cares for us
Which makes us mad and sigh.

In the end it's not all bad
Even when you're feeling mad
When it seems your parents aren't fair
They only do it because they care!

Amber Burgess-Game (13)

THE FOURTEEN-YEAR-OLD ADULT

If you are young, twelve or less,
You may well ask what's ahead?
What's it like to be a teenager?

Well my friend, I'll tell you now,
I'll update you on why and how.
The moods, the changes, they're all ahead,
The whole life that's led,
By the adults, the grown-ups, whichever you prefer.
You are the future generation, they all refer.
'I know what it's like,' they say
'To change into a different way
Of life you lead, responsibility is the key
To growing up, to be just like me!'
But who said we want to grow up
And begin to do this grown-up stuff?
To get jobs, pay bills, just wait!
I'm only fourteen, for goodness sake!
I've got my life and it's just fine,
We'll discuss this another time.
At the moment, I think I'll just
Go and have fun, at my age, it's a must!

So, if you're young, twelve or less,
You may well ask what's ahead,
What's it like to be a teenager?
Well, that all depends on you!

Laura Blundell (14)

LADY LUCK

Future lies ahead,
While your past lies behind.
Search ahead if you wish
No guessing what you'll find.

Lady Luck has her fancies,
So does death intone.
We who walk the woven path
We walk it alone!

Past, present, future;
All combine together
As millennia, aeons pass.
As mankind do endeavour.

Time passes, God stands absent,
Daydreaming. always asking about the same obscurity:
Life . . . or death.
Man stands in insecurity.

A chance to live, a chance to die.
Lady Luck makes her decrees and we can do naught
But slavishly follow.
Into the future, the people have sought.

This is luck, destiny, this is fate.
This fortune, chance, this is time.
This is life, this is death.
Yin and Yang
Life . . . or death?

Layla Saggers (13)

A Hero

A hero doesn't fly
A hero doesn't have super strength
A hero doesn't shoot lasers from his eyes

A hero doesn't wear a cape
A hero doesn't have a utility belt
A hero doesn't hide behind a mask

A hero doesn't fight evil
A hero doesn't have mortal enemies
A hero doesn't have a sidekick to help him

A hero has a helmet
A hero wears a badge
A hero gives his life for others

A hero is a fire-fighter
A hero is a police officer
A hero is a paramedic

A hero *is* every rescue worker
Who helped to save lives
In the September 11th attack

A hero *is* every Rescue Worker
Who died to save lives
In the September 11th attack

That is what a true *hero* is!

Adam Sankey (14)

NATURE'S CALL

Can you hear the raindrops
Falling gently on the ground?
Or see that flower bud in April
Magically, without a sound?

Can you hear the blackbird sing,
And witness the delight it brings?
Or see the leaves floating freely?
Golds, bronzes, reds and coppers, all such a wonderful scenery.

Can you hear the whisper of a soft and hushed breeze
As it softly whistles through the trees?
And can you see that peaceful, clear blue sea?
It brings more calming thoughts to me.

Can you hear the crashing of the waves
As they splash up against the walls of the caves?
And can you see the fish swim in fright
Avoiding certain things all through the night?

Can you hear the silent sway of the grass?
The beautiful crystal green, it's growing so fast.
Can you spot the bird flying gracefully in the sky?
As you watch it go high and high.

Nature's special in every way,
So don't take it for granted every day.
Be grateful for what you've been given,
And thank God for the world which you live in.

Leann Macaulay (14)

A Day In The Life

Thursday morning 8.05
Now it's time to look alive,
Stop all that magic in your head
It's time to go to school instead.

You're not well liked in Class 4.4
The other kids deem you a bore.
Boys talk girls and girls talk boys,
Still babies playing with their toys -
Except these ones have ring tones.

You're huddled in the corner of the class,
Neglecting chemistry, RE and maths
Thinking Harry, Lyra, Bowman and Jed,
The only way to forget the neds.

Teachers talk exams and tests;
'This is no time for fun and jests,
You have to think the way *we* want
K and U - you know nought!'

Exams are what they've always been,
Life is exactly what it seems.
There are no wizards in the gloom
No evil forces planning doom
No knights to save you from form room . . .

Is this all there is?

Fiona Kayes (14)

I HAD A DREAM

I had a dream, a glorious dream
And it was wonderful, yes just wonderful,
It kept me alive all through the winter
And it helped me see the truth that's before me,
I thought I'd never see the day you left me,
But it was wonderful and I enjoyed it,
You'd only hurt me if I stayed with you,
So it's for the best that you are gone.
My friends, they cared for me
And helped me through the hard times and the good times,
We had some good times, but mostly bad ones
And I knew that you were with another woman,
She must be special for you to leave me,
As you said that I was special,
You said to me when I first met you,
That you would never cheat, you'd always love me.
I must've been a fool to not see through you.
My friends, they warned me against people like you
But I ignored them and then fell for you.
I don't know why, but I just did.
So is she special? This other girl?
Or are you using her? Just like you used me!
Cos if you are, then I will tell her
And she will leave you, like you left me.
I had a dream, a glorious dream
And it was wonderful, just wonderful.

Claire Sime (14)

THE SPACE

Inside my small mind,
Much of the capacity
Is a waste of time.
You never use this space
And it's not just mine,
Everyone's affected,
We're one of a kind.
That is why
When teachers talk,
People's minds wander,
Hopeless in the dark.
You don't listen,
To what's being said,
Because half your space
Is just brain dead!
So take heed of these words,
And snap out of the trance,
Set your space free,
Make it dance.
You never know what may happen,
If you let the space free,
Just remember,
You got the advice from me!

Harriet Brown (13)

FUTURE

What will happen when I leave school?
Will I go to college?
Will I get a job
Or will I end up broke?
Will I stay in this country

Or will I travel the world?
Will I marry
Or stay alone?
How uncertain our future is,
Let's try and enjoy the present.

Rhiannon Beckett (13)

THE CIRCLE OF LIFE

When I sit on that hillside
Wherever it may be,
I just get that feeling
Of being completely free.

All the usual burdens
Of life from day to day
Are lifted from my shoulders
Carried far, far away.

Arising from that hillside,
Rising forth to face the way.
The way to strive, to fall, to live
The only real way.

For to sit forever
Is fine from time to time
To cherish every moment
The trophy of my climb.

But to sit forever
Is fantasy not life.
And fantasy, eternally
Evolves with equal strife.

Katie Webb (15)

A WORLD THAT CANNOT BE TOUCHED

A dream is like a distant star;
It seems so close, but yet so far,
That world of happiness that cannot be touched
A place in time where you cannot be watched.
A destination lost in fantasy,
The land that's made for him and me.
A dream can conjure such temptation,
The star that holds my inspiration.
My ambition there to be fulfilled,
An existence where I'll be willed.
A time to think and a time to be
Something more than just simply me.
Dreams are merely a corner of your mind
Being set free, led by the blind.
A universe that's too surreal,
Just understand the way I feel.

Katie Round (15)

DEATH

He wears a big black cape
Over his head it would drape

His face is hidden
The hands are forbidden

He leans upon his pole vault stick
Made from wood, fine and slick

Like a night sky minus the moon
He covers himself in his cape like a black cocoon

Enclosed in an intoxicating smell
He is the guy who will send you to Heaven or Hell!

James Beggs (13)

LIFE

I live in a world with all my mates,
They fix me up with awful dates,
We have a laugh now and then,
Seeing all these gorgeous men.
But family means a lot to me,
Although they are mad and crazy!
They give me a hug when I'm down,
I know they'll always be around,
My worst enemy is my brother,
To be honest, there is no other!
He argues and teases with me all day long,
Every day he smells of a pong,
My ambition is to draw,
Skirts, trousers and lots more.
A fashion designer - that's what I'll be,
They don't believe but they'll see.
In years to come the future will be,
A different world for you and me!

Alyssa Garrard (13)

MY FACE

What a face I've got
And that's not in a good way
I've got hazel eyes
And a mouth as big as a subway.
My nose is just disgusting
I've always wished for another
But then again
There's no point in moaning
They were given by my mother!

Natalie L Gamble (13)

HAPPINESS

Happiness is like sunshine
glowing and bright
contrasting against the sky blue
occasionally hidden
by dark clouds
casting gloominess with shadows,
then it reappears
lighting up the world
when night
draws in
the rosiness fades away,
excitement wears off
as the great orb of fire sinks
into the horizon.
Stars come out
twinkling brightly,
constant reminders,
smiles lighting up the night.
Then the moon
reflecting the very essence
of the sun.
Happiness always exists

Olivia Wilson (14)

TEENAGE STUFF

My teenage yeas have been brilliant so far,
At 13 I wanted to be a pop star,
I thought I was the next Britney Spears,
So I would get my karaoke out and sing as her.

Once turned 14 I thought I was all grown up
Oh boy did I have a shock
School got harder then exams arrived
I got so stressed out I nearly cried.

Now 15, school's nearly over,
I want to travel the world and see all over
Europe first, then exotic beaches
Try the unique cuisine, fruits and peaches.

The future's to come I've not decided
But I've got plenty of time to grow up and find it.
It could be good, it could be bad,
But I will always have the past to look back on and be glad!

Zoë Brookes (15)

I'm Not A Bully

Mum's always told me I'm involved with the wrong people,
She calls them bullies.
We're not bullies . . . really. We just tease
They're wicked to hang out with,
We do all sorts of things . . .
Muck around with trolleys, travel without buying tickets . . .
And we tease people, just for fun.
They don't care.
Last night, we were out for a laugh, out for a joke.
Boffy Janie from our school is walking down the street
Hurrying past, hoping to go unnoticed, this should be a laugh.

I'm pushed to the edge of the kerb,
'Come on Luce, show her how we deal with teacher's pets,'
. . . someone hands me a knife.
All eyes are upon me, saying
'Come on, it's a joke, it's just a bit of fun!'
I'm still holding a knife . . .
No, verbal teasing is one thing,
Violence is another.

I guess Mum's right.

Bianca Belby (15)

YOU SUFFER TOO
(From the point of view of the victim - talking to the bully.)

You think you're so big
But really you're small,
You think you're so great
That you never will fall.

You taunt me and hurt me
But the bruises will fade,
You like me to suffer
You make me afraid.

You think I'm a coward
Maybe it's true.
Although you may seem tough
The coward is you.

People admire you
They don't know what you do
I know the truth
And I'd hate to be you.

Each night you go through hours of worry
You've always got something to hide
You make me promise to keep it a secret
But you know I'm not on your side.

You're probably very unhappy
So it makes you behave as you do
I wonder why you do it
How does it satisfy you?

You always make me suffer
You seem quite proud when you do
Don't think I'm blind to your problems
I know that you suffer, too.

Claire Phelps (15)

TEENAGE YEARS

Hormones are buzzing
  Spots are bursting,
    Hair is getting greasy.

Peer pressure, anxiety,
  Unanswered questions,
    What did that dream mean?

Do my friends like me?
  They are maturing faster,
    I go along with the crowd.

I'm fat, I'm ugly,
  I need to diet,
    Will he ever fancy me?

My temper rising,
  I'm going to burst,
    What do I do with myself?

My hair's not right,
  My make-up's wrong,
    I've got to keep up with the fashion.

Pressure to buy,
  Pressure to succeed,
    Pressure, pressure, pressure!

Life's a whirl,
  A big competition,
    I feel I'm going to burst.

I look in the mirror,
  Who do I see?
    A teenager. Me!

Phillipa Smith (14)

TRAMPY LADY

Oh trampy lady
I see you every day
Oh trampy lady
You make me run away
Oh trampy lady
I see you on the wall
Oh trampy lady
Watch you don't fall
Oh trampy lady
Look at the clothes you wear
Oh trampy lady
You need to brush your hair
Oh trampy lady
I hate you so much
Oh trampy lady
Please do not touch
Oh trampy lady
I try to stay out of reach
Oh trampy lady
Clean your clothes in bleach.

Katie Brown (13)

AMBITIONS OF THE FUTURE

There are so many things I wish to be,
To be a doctor is one.
'You saved my life,' a patient will say
And my feelings tell me I've won.

There are so many things I wish to be,
To be a lawyer is two.
'Well done,' and 'thank you,' a client will say,
'Yes, and well done to you.'

There are so many things I wish to be,
A better friend is three.
'Thanks for being there,' she'll say,
I'm glad they'll think that of me.

There are so many things I wish to be,
But my biggest ambition of all
Is to be no one else because deep down,
I like who I am on the whole!

Laura Royle (13)

NATURE IS A WONDERFUL THING

Beautiful to those who can see,
Sweet smelling to those who can smell,
Full of amazing texture for those who can touch,
A marvellous band to those who can hear
And a cocktail of flavours for those who can taste,
Put these together and nature's your answer,
So why do we want to destroy it?

Why swap something so unique to our planet,
For the high rise buildings, polluted air and concrete jungles?
Is it a fair trade, I think not, there are so many issues
Yet half our population seem to overlook them.

We should preserve what's left before humans densely
over populate the world's natural wonders, for their comforts.

The future can be good, think of the great, great
Grandchildren - no rainforests, no fuels, no countryside.

Please stop and help make the world a better place.

Kerry Hodges (14)

REVELATIONS

'Be prettier,' you said,
As you took one step after another,
Further away.
You're looking at me with that grin on your face,
The one that scares me like no other.
Who would have known?
Endings are always the same
And I'm still here,
Waiting for the day where these words won't
Get so caught up inside me,
The day these lips do something more than kill me.
Because of your habits I'm knee deep in something I can't find.
I hate you,
I hate all the things you do.
I hate that I'm so in love with you.

Jennifer Law (14)

LIFE

Desks, desks, sitting at desks.
Tests, tests, we're taking tests,
All our lives, we're taking tests;
Double SATs, GCSEs, Degrees,
Tests, tests, taking tests.

Pencil, paper, rubber they say,
Number 2 pencil only, OK?
Turn over! Start!
Five minutes to go!

When do we play?
When do we learn?
No time to watch the clouds go by.

David Harsent (14)

TEENAGE YEARS

Changes in my body and changes in my mind,
Changes in my feelings, my childhood left behind,
I feel about some people like I have never felt before,
Some of these stronger feelings are just too strong to ignore,
I'm changing from a little girl into my teenage years
And with this change comes tension and plenty teenage fears,
My life is changing every day to suit my growing mind
And to my many questions the answers I will find,
The people in society think we are all the same,
A few unruly people who give all teen's a bad name,
The adults working in the shops, drawing dirty looks,
No need to be suspicious we are not all filthy crooks,
Because of all this changing we are so misunderstood,
The smallest things annoy us and can turn around our mood,
Mood swings come and mood swings go, then swing right out of here,
But they will swing right back again, so pray you are not near.

Laura Mathieson (13)

DAYDREAMING

I looked out of the window in class and I started staring at the grass.
My mind was happy, it was free. I looked again the grass was the sea.
I looked into the sea at the funny little creatures,
                    I wasn't paying attention to my teachers.
They called me and shook me but I was in a trance. I wanted
                        to go into the sea while I had a chance.
I blinked but the sea wasn't there, the sea had gone into thin air.
The creatures weren't there anymore, the sea was gone it
                        was once again the moor.
I looked out of the window in class, and started staring at the grass.

Sam Dixon (13)

SAYING GOODBYE

Have you ever experienced loneliness
Or are you one of the popular ones?
Have you ever said goodbye
To someone who never meant to hurt you?

Just yesterday I heard a fact,
That my best friend was leaving,
I never thought this day would come,
But who was I deceiving?

She'll be off to dancing school,
I am proud of her really,
It's just that deep down inside I'll miss her
And our contact will always end with sincerely.

It looks to me, that's just to me,
That I'll be losing out,
My other friends are paired in twos
And it's as though I have not been sorted out.

I will be sad and be happy,
To see her leave us all behind,
But I must remember it's not quite over,
She'll be coming home sometimes!

Have you ever experienced loneliness
Or are you one of the popular ones?
I am having to say goodbye
To my best friend, Natalie.

Harriet McGregor (14)

007 FOREVER

When the world is under threat by Blofeld and his cat,
Or even Oddjob and his steel rimmed hat.
Then there's Goldfinger in his plane and Scaramanga in his boat,
These villains travel in anything, so please take note.
They travel and travel they just go anywhere,
But these villains still attack from land, sea and air.

But there's a man you can always count on,
Whose work in the field is second to none.
He'll foil the bad guys cunning plan,
With the help of Q - the gadget man.

He just leaps into action with his PPK,
That will get a few bad guys outta the way.
A tiny gadget will see him through,
Out of the bad guys horrid HQ.

Then off to the casino this slick man goes,
Driven in a bright green rolls.
He walks into the joint and a sound he heard,
'I'll have a Martini, shaken not stirred!'

Back to HQ for our man has won,
Thanks to him it's a job well done.
But this is a man, of which the world is fond,
Who is he?
He is Bond, James Bond.

Simon Taylor (15)

UNTITLED

It's hard being a teenage girl,
You feel mixed up and confused.
You wonder about yourself and the future,
Sometimes you feel on top of the world
And other times you feel down in the dumps.

I wonder why girls want to be older
And when they are old, they want to be young,
My friends like to look older, I don't know why,
I look my age, I'll grow up in time,
I'm not into fashion, I have my own style.

I like listening to music,
It helps me to think and relax,
It helps me clear my head,
When I'm worried or upset.
I wonder why other girls
Don't seem to worry like I do.

Although it's difficult, I like being a teenager,
There are good things about it,
This poem is a bit mixed up, but it's how I feel.

Zoe Seager (15)

WAR

War is the Son of Hatred,
War is the Key to Death.
It has no identity or form,
Yet, it still is Dread.

It is like a jigsaw,
With pieces of hatred, anger and revenge,
When put together,
They make destruction,
They make war.

Each letter of war stands for something,
It stands for what war is about,
Each letter stands for
Winning, Annihilation and Revenge.

War means brother vs brother,
War means nothing,
But, war also means murder.

Qasim Riaz

LIFE IS ALL AND ALL IS LIFE

Life is like a fairy tale,
Life is like a dream,
Life is like a nightmare,
Life is like a scream,
Life is all
And all is life,
What have we to gain?
For there is good and bad,
There is the merry and sad,
There is rich and poor,
There is black and white,
There is Protestant and Catholic,
But aren't we all the same?
For what is colour or religion,
When we're all the same?
Why can't we share what we have
And live in peace and harmony
And never hurt or mock each other
And live as a nation
Not as a war?
For life is us
And we are life.

Oliver McAfee (13)

A Grumpy, Lazy (Normal) Teenager

When I was ten,
I used to say,
Three years to go,
Till I can show,
How grumpy and lazy I am.

When I was eleven,
I used grumpy expressions,
But I still didn't seem,
What I wanted to be,
A grumpy, lazy teenager.

When I was twelve,
I started waking up late,
I was happy all the time,
But then the bell chimed,
I was about to become a teenager.

Finally I was thirteen,
My best ever dream,
But! My spots started showing
And I was turning too grumpy,
Why couldn't I stay a non-teen?

Karan Ramanay (13)

Painful Memory

Painful memories fill an angry sky,
Jealousy and hate flood an empty heart,
My body is a jigsaw,
The missing piece is my heart,
Happiness is a thing of the past,
Anger and deceit lie here now.

Claire Tamplin (14)

IT'S A TEENAGER'S LIFE!

Suddenly my life,
Tilted upside down,
You never know what to expect
I'm a teenager now.

Up and down,
Like a rapid stream,
Hormones getting out of hand
Makes me want to scream.

The world has turned around,
My room is a mess,
My music must stay cool,
My fashion must be best.

Now that I am different,
For my sister, Dad and Mum,
It's very, very hard,
Because I'm an unreliable bomb.

School becomes difficult,
For my friends as well,
Glad that I'm not alone,
So we are all in Hell!

The world we are in,
Our future lies ahead,
Good or bad,
But dreams are in our heads.

So lots of things happen and will
Spots, fashion, getting frights,
Oh well, let's just say,
It's a teenager's life!

Holly Trethewey (13)

MY FAMILY!

My brother is a pain
And he has no brain.
My sister is funny
And has loads of money.
My cousin is a laugh
But she needs a good bath.
My grandad is sweet
And is very neat.
My uncle is called Pete
But he's got smelly feet.
My auntie is great
And is a very good mate.
My mum is kind.
My dad is blind.
My nan is rich with a garden like
A football pitch.
I like my gran
But she looks like a man,
But I don't give a damn,
Because that's the way I am!

Laura Ellis (13)

PAIN

What can I say or do to make this feeling go away?
I don't think I can take anymore.
I feel as if tears from my eyes are about to pour.
I've never in my life felt like this before.
I can't handle the pain my heart's telling me to ignore.
Something's holding me back and keeping me
Strong, but who knows? I could be wrong.
All I want to do is to write my feelings into a song
To keep me holding on until my pain is gone.

Jeshma Raithatha (15)

LIFE IS A POEM

Although you'd never know it Buddy
I'm a kind of poet,
I could sit here with my note pad all day.
Scribbling down my poems,
About young Sherlock Holmes,
With no one to get in my way.
I'd go through good and bad times,
Making up these great rhymes
And I'd show them to you one day.
When I'm standing on the stage,
Reading from my plays,
You'll be cheering me on all the way.
When I really do shine,
I'll make it to the big time
And bring my work home for you.
When I'm rich and famous,
Poetry is not the greatest,
There is nothing left for me to do.
I thought poems were smashing,
But now they're out of fashion,
My only friend now is you.
Now I've blew all my money,
I'll be glad you're here sonny,
Spend the rest of my days with you.

Robert McMillan (13)

BULLIES

You wake up and remember
What day it is today,
You do not want to get up
For today is Monday.
You leave the house early
So you are not late,
But walk to school slowly,
Because you know they'll be waiting at the gates.
You're upset and scared,
So you truant from school,
You lose education,
That's a silly thing to do.
Bullies pick on people
Because they think they're tough,
They call you names
And take your stuff.
Come what may
Never wish your life away.
If you are being bullied
You must let someone know,
Because bullies will not let you go.
Everyone out there,
You are not alone,
Someone does care.

Holly Turnbull (13)

IT'S A HARD LIFE!

It's hard, sometimes it's too hard
But then it's fun and you're happier than anyone.
But then something's bound to happen!
And your feet are back on the ground and you're mad at someone.
It's hard being a teenager.
You get shouted at for things you thought didn't even exist.
You get told that because now you're old you've gained
Something called responsibility.
You get nagged and screamed at to go to your room!
When for the last three days that's where you've always been!
But the only person who noticed you were gone was Tom the cat.

It's hard being a teenager,
One minute you're laughing
And then you're back in your room with the cat,
But you can't understand why mum gets so mad?
All you did was hit your brother, it wasn't that hard at all!

It's hard being a teenager!
Oh yes! When you turn 13 there's no going back!
You're no longer a kid, and you can't say you're adult,
You're just a teenager!
When one day it feels the whole world against you!
Then madly in love with you and can't stop hugging you!

It's hard being a teenager! But fun being me!

Leanne Roost (13)

163

ALONE

I drown my sorrows deep inside,
To a corner I run and hide.
Every day my mind takes its toll,
As I am the perfect student role.
Everybody always expects the same,
But all I want is the popular fame.
To grow up to be on TV,
Go out in the world and be me.
Not to be stuck in a boring, brainbox job,
Only for me to sit and sob.
I want to be the black sheep,
To take great, big, daring leaps.
Around the world I want to be known
And scream in a deafening tone.
So everyone will stop and stare,
Drop everything and look over there.
Where I am standing fulfilling my dreams,
Bring out the best in me.
Sadly it's school tomorrow
And again I can feel my sorrow.
Back to reality I return,
Where, in secret, my fire slowly burns.

Norah Almola (14)

AS TIME GOES BY

Tiny hands and tiny feet
And chubby little cheeks.
Twinkling eyes, sticky-out ears
And tufts of hair in peaks.

The smell of baby lotion
On a soft and silky bum.
Warm milk and icky baby food
And a dried up shrivelled thumb.

From playgroup to big school,
Then off to college and tests.
First teething, childhood and the terrible teens,
Up until they fly the nest.

We won't forget the years we had,
Or the ones that are still to come.
But a tear comes to my eye,
As they leave, one by one.

Daisy Taylor (13)

UNDER MY SISTER'S BED

Under my sister's bed
you will find:
Over-used tissues, sticking to the bedposts.
An out-of-date sandwich.
Mouldy make-up which she spilled water on
and didn't wipe off.

You can find:
Cat hairs sticking to her dirty laundry.
Those leftover bits of food from all the sleepovers.
That old Barbie typewriter she was going
to give to me.

Under her bed:
There are piles of magazines of Take That
and Westlife.
All the postcards she bought back from our holiday.
The last bit of half-eaten rock, she forgot.

Don't dare look under my sister's bed,
For sure it will make your stomach churn.
It did my mums, when she saw it.

Sophie Godliman (12)

A Day In The Life Of Me

Get up in the morning,
Rub sleep from my eyes,
Pull on some clothes,
Make up homework lies.

Look in the mirror,
What do you see?
One teen girl getting ready
For another dull day in the life of me.

Finally out the door,
Another dull day in a less than cool school,
I'm thinking,
While I'm walking,
With Jenny and talking.

I get to school and meet my friends,
Full of laughter that will never end,
I glance at my timetable to see what I'm in
And when I know, my smile's pretty thin.

Then the last bell rings,
A thousand voices sing,
Walk to the bus stop and wait for Jenny.

Walk all the way back,
My tie done slack,
I know I moan about my school,
But really, I think it is quite cool,
Meeting my friends,
Arguments and amends,
New things to learn and see
And it's the end of another cool day
In the cool life of me.

Victoria Kinnaird (14)

TEENAGERS

T exting on our phone,
   Makes everybody groan.
E arly mornings!
   They get us yawning.
E arly night!
   We'll avoid with all our might.
N ever do anything uncool,
   For fear of looking like a fool.
A nd we love to listen to our CDs,
   Though we're often asked to, 'Turn it down . . . please.'
G oing to the shops,
   Is something we like lots.
E very day we try to look our best,
   So we look as cool as the rest.
R aging zits!
   We wish they'd quit!
S pots, moody, grumpy, and loud,
   We are teenagers and we're proud!

Chloe Booty (13)

MY TRUE NORTH STAR

You are the guardian angel of my soul, you protect me,
To all my emotions, only you hold the key,
You comfort and guide me in ways I sometimes never see.

In the darkness that surrounds me you are the light,
You are the stirring warmth in the blackness of night,
With you in my heart, I never feel my troubles, my pain or plight.

I was scared and you've banished my fear,
When I lost my happiness in pearly drops, you dried every tear,
Now I can't imagine life without you near.

Nicola Cowell (15)

ONE LIFE

Silence.
The soft, anxious, underlying thoughts of nothing.
Innocence teaching us nothing; disaster struck.
One life crashed to a heart-wrenching halt,
While others crumbled, lying crushed, open to
The world of anguish.

Suddenly, terrified screams hit the ears of all those who could hear,
As sudden as the crash itself.
And nothing could prepare us for the worst.

That one life. I never knew it. I never will.
On that dreadful night, one life and lots more torn.
I will remember it always, in my heart and mind.
One life.

The crash.

Georgina Hamil (14)

THE POWER OF ANGER AND SADNESS

Why must I smile for a photograph when I want to cry?
How can a murderer watch the innocent die?
When did machines take over God's Earth
And why is money more than it's worth?
Why did goodness and purity turn to mud?
How strong is hatred when it leads to the scent of blood?
Does a broken hope always have to end with a day of weeping?
What happened to the pleasant dreams while we were sleeping?
We are overshadowed and haunted with lies
And are too blind to really see the truth with our eyes
Would the world be different if Eve hadn't eaten the poisonous fruit?
Our body has a heart we need to use just as a plant has a root.

Natalie Solgala-Kaz (14)

GROWING PAINS

When I was only five years old,
I began to read and write,
School had begun, learning was fun
And I worked with all my might.

Now I'm thirteen, I'm not quite so keen,
I don't adore school at all,
Maths is a bore and German's a chore,
The classrooms are all far too small.

When I was only five years old,
Home was a great place to be,
I didn't fight, was always polite
And enjoyed just being me.

Now I'm thirteen, I don't know why,
I'm always in a mood,
It makes me mad and sometimes sad,
When I'm told not to be so rude.

When I was only five years old,
Life was easy for me,
I never hurried, was rarely worried
And was pretty much carefree.

Now I'm thirteen, life is more mean,
Myself - I sometimes hate.
Am I OK? Will my spots go away?
I wonder, what is my fate?

I've grown in many ways since I was five,
Examples, there's quite a few,
There's far too many to list
And I've still got lots to do!

Natalie Shinkwin (13)

A Child's Perspective

The water shone like lost gems now found
While we on the beach, wrestled each other to the ground
The sun showered us all day with its rays
There isn't anything to beat lazy summer days
Being with friends, smiling, laughing, having fun,
All individuals, but as a group we are one.
Inevitably the moon rose high in the sky
And we all understand for a while it was goodbye.
But fear not as morning brings new light
When we no longer fear the coming of the night
Naiveté is a gift for our lack of years
It helps us to live a summer without adult fears
We admit we can be wrong and often make adults riled
But where would the world be without the mind of a child?

Thomas Stevenson (15)

Planeasaurus

Planes are not all there
in the sky so high.
Walking down the road one day,
a plane comes down
from the sky so high.
Large, silver, grey and old.
Sun shining on wings that fold
swooping, soaring,
from the sky so high.
Looking closer the plane is not all there,
only a bird flying,
in the sky so high.

Luke Chard (13)

THE PROBLEMS WITH BEING A TEEN!

Waking up in the morning,
is the hardest thing to do,
to us it still feels like night-time,
but to them a daytime zoo.

They shouted at me for getting my nose pierced,
which I think's really unfair,
'It's only a little hole,' I said,
but to them it's a living nightmare.

The night before was a blast,
but the after affects did show,
all those lovely red, juicy spots,
that made me say 'Oh no!'

My mascara is everywhere,
it's all in my hair,
my roots are growing pretty quick,
I just look like an ugly bear.

I'm sick of being a teenager,
my life's too tough,
getting told off for the simplest things
like being in a huff.

However at only thirteen,
I have all the rest to come,
only another six years to go,
oh what a shame for my mum!

Kineta Kelsall (13)

I AM...

I am all I see,
My poor three-legged cat hopping along,
Jammy adverts selling stuff which doesn't even work,
Fireworks flashing above the hedge.

I am all I hear,
The slamming of doors
And shouting soon after.
The crocky purr of Kitty always cheers me up,
My gerbil chewing at yet another cardboard box.

I am all I taste,
Lovely lemon curd and Marmite sandwiches.
Greasy chips fresh from the newspaper,
The horrible taste of dog hairs in your mouth.

I am all I remember,
The pain of breaking legs,
Embarrassing photos, my mum used to show,
Putting my two beloved fish in the pond.

I am all I've been taught,
Always put things back where you got them from,
Never use the last stamp from the box,
Stop stressing over nothing.

I am all I think,
Deep, dark secrets,
Catchy tunes that stay in your head
I am like a star shining brightly,
But sometimes flicker or shadowed by a cloud,
I am the star of the galaxy.

Bridgette Curtis (13)

TERRORIST ATTACK ON AMERICA

It was a normal day in America, planes were roaming the sky,
But no one knew what was to happen next, how many were to die.

It was at 9 o'clock it happened, the day that lives were changed,
But as the planes were getting closer, the Twin Towers
were well in range.

At first one came from nowhere, hitting the sixty-third floor,
The stairs were cramped, the elevators full, and there was no way
out of the door.

People were jumping from windows, free-falling from the sky,
It was a terrible sight, people full up with fright,
knowing that they were to die.

Then another plane came, hitting with a sudden burst,
The impact here was greater, as the second tower went first.

The towers were sadly demolished, after being so high,
The rubble seemed so endless, clouds of dust ruled the sky.

But they couldn't move the rubble, for people were still alive,
Even if they were left to get out, it is doubtful they'd survive.

Who could have done such a terrible thing?
Someone who must have been mad,
Afghanistan's Bin Laden holds the blame, security must have been bad.

How did the hijackers get on the plane? I'll bet they were very amused,
Surely the pilot wouldn't hand over the plane, so there must have been
some weapons used.

It wasn't just the towers they hit, the Pentagon too,
Think what it's done to the nation of America,
imagine if it happened to you.

Thomas Stone (13)

FAMILY

My family is such a pain,
They are so loud, which drives me insane;
Neighbours complain every day,
They haven't stopped, now it's May;
They always have fights,
Which gives me lots of frights;
I think they're going to drive me mad,
But what can I do, it's just so bad;
Whilst they were fighting, they broke my chain,
I really got angry and I said that they needed to check their brains;
People walked past and said, 'What's going on in that yard?'
I just said, 'Some family problems, read that card;'
Mum and daughter take each other's side,
Dad and son, always take this as rides;
I'll be spending a fortune in this house,
It's like I've been turned into a mouse;
24 hours, that's their daily routine
And that is how they've always been.

Dimple Chauhan (13)

WHERE IS MY HOME?

Chimpanzee with doleful eyes
Looks up into the grey smoky skies
Where will you roam?
Now they are burning your home
What is your plan?
Now they have ruined your land.

Along came man, with ideas so grand
What is he doing to your homeland?
Up-rooting trees and cutting down weeds
Where do you lead your family to feed?

174

The farmers want roads
They want to make money
They ignore nature's code
Oh chimp, it's not funny!

Natalie Alcock (15)

EARTH

15,000 million years ago
our universe was created
from a tiny ball of fire,
a raging inferno of orange, red and yellow.
It exploded with a ferocious *bang*
sending particles of matter
flying like aeroplanes everywhere.
Our galaxy, the Milky Way was formed
and our planet came into existence.
The land rose up like the sun on a new day,
plants began to grow,
turning into trees and flowers as if by magic.
The sea covered the world like a big marine jelly,
full of wildlife.
Scaly, sleek beasts, we now call fish
started to swim like clouds in the sky.
They evolved into dinosaurs
like a cake rising in the oven.
Catastrophe struck, the dinosaurs perished.
The human race was born.
We grew, adults learning to walk and talk
like toddlers.
Now we live in a world of computers and
telecommunications.
Life used to be so simple on the Earth.

Eleanor Tate (13)

TEENAGERS

Teenage lives are often muddled
Messed around and homework troubled
College courses in your mind
Leaving childhood far behind
Fashion conscious all the while
Homework growing pile by pile

Deadlines to catch
Standards to match
Friends to make
Friends to lose
Life goes on
Whatever you choose

Teenage crime
Higher than ever
People may be
Not so clever
Teenage lives are often muddled
Messed around and homework troubled
But that's life.

Alice Neve (14)

A TRUE FRIEND

You are the air I breathe, the sun I see
You mean everything to me.

I am never alone when I think of you,
You are the centre of everything I do.

When I am old and sitting in my rocking chair,
I know that I'll be happy, as long as you are there.

Paul Doherty (15)

Love = Suicide

I tell you I love you and wait for your reply,
But you shove your hands in your pockets and look up at the sky.
I tell you I love you more than anything else in the world,
But you laugh and wave at the person behind me.
I tear out my heart and lay it on the table for you to see,
It is torn into tatters with blood spurting out of the cracks,
The love inside me turns into hate,
Hate for you and hate for me and hate for this world too.
As I pick up a knife, the blade shimmers in the sunlight,
But the sun is red,
Red with wet blood,
Your blood or my blood?
You tell me you love me
But I don't hear you.
It's too late,
Because I'm already gone.

Rachael Holm (14)

You!

You make me laugh, you make me smile,
When days are long and hard to get by.
We used to walk, we used to talk,
But now only get time to stare, like a hawk.
We used to be friends, we used to be close,
But now separated by a greater force.
We might meet now, we might meet never,
But I know we'll always be close together.
You'll always listen, you'll always care,
But what happened is just not fair.

Samantha Jane Griffith-Thomas (14)

THE ONLY JOB FOR ME

I'll not be an optician
Or an electrician.
I won't be a psychologist
Or an archaeologist.

I'll not be a bin man
Or the daily postman.
I won't be a referee
Or star on TV.

I'll not be a plumber
Or an Olympic runner.
I won't be a singer
Or a church bell ringer.

I'll not be a news reader
Or a garden weeder.
I won't be a hairdresser
Or a college professor.

I'll not be a zookeeper
Or a street sweeper.
Because the only job for me
Is writing poetry!

Philip Gordon (13)

RELIGION

I think there are too many religions in the world,
Every single one of them should be hurled.
Why can't everyone get on well?
Because you're making this world a living Hell.

There's so much fighting in July
And there's no logical reason why.
Summer holidays are destroyed,
Which is making people very annoyed.

Pensioners attacked in their own homes,
So many dangerous people in this world roam.
Many people want to know,
Why those prisoners were let go.

If it were up to me,
I'd lock them up and throw away the key.
Why can't everyone become one
And make this a better place for your daughter or son?

Claire Harper (13)

COUNTRYSIDE

In the country,
Is there anywhere as calm?
The peacefulness of the slowly swaying trees,
The tranquillity of the solitary silence.

In summer, the warmth brings happiness.
The shade of an oak, so fierce.
In rain or after
The smell of fresh and renewed living.

In winter, when snow falls,
A white, carpeted landscape.
Trees covered, branches sagging,
Ice coated lakes, seem to softly sing.

In autumn, each tree, a kaleidoscope of colour,
The ground, a damp home for creatures.
As a nut falls heavily to the ground,
A squirrel comes to claim it.

This world, so different, yet so similar,
Is a refuge
For time alone, for peace of mind,
This place provides it all.

Laura Blackburn (13)

MY LIFE IS THE WEATHER

My life is a hurricane.
It brews up ideas
And blows them away again.

My life is a tornado.
It spins round my brain.
Memories, maths and moments are thrown around by it.

My life is a storm.
The thunder booms and the lightning strikes.
Nowhere is safe.

My life is a blizzard.
I am blown in every direction
Until I settle amongst everyone else.

My life is a cloud.
I float around throughout the day.
I am in a different world.

My life is the sunshine.
I am warm and friendly
But I can scorch and singe.

My life is the weather!

Katie Higgins (13)

A LONELY THOUGHT

The world is an endless circle,
Your pain goes on and on,
Every hurting punch will hurt everyone.

Your peace is only a centimetre,
You only get one bit,
Does anybody really love you?
What does love get?

Each heart has a key,
But where have the keys been put?
Only one person can find them,
Where does that person live?

Lydia Andrews (13)

THE TRUTH ABOUT TEENAGERS!

'Clean up your room!
Make up your bed!'
So many orders get lost in my head!

'Do your homework, right now!'
But it always makes me dizzy,
When I've no time to stop and I'm always busy.

'Look clean and smart!
And do as you're told!'
Why do mums have to nag and scold?

We know where stuff is,
So why clean our room?
It's a living nightmare, a tale of doom!

And making my bed,
Is really not right,
When I'll just sleep in it again tonight!

I try to behave
But really how can you
When the whole world is blaming it on you?

Teens can't win,
Whoever they may be,
But one day we'll rebel, and parents will see!

Heidi Robus (13)

WHERE O' WHERE ARE THEIR HUMAN RIGHTS?

Thump! Kick! Slish! Slash!
My poor Daddy has got the lash
Kick! Thump! Thump! Kick!
I've been beaten with 'the stick'

Human Rights should be
For all to have and share
But whilst we're being tortured
You just stop, stand and stare

My mum has been in prison
For poems that she read
The Government didn't like it
And now . . . guess what? She's dead

My older brother Samuel
Was tortured and he died
For disobeying a Government Rule
Where's his Human Rights?
Denied!

I've been beaten and abused
All my feelings are confused
I wonder what life holds for me
Certainly not peace and harmony

Human beings should be free
Not spending life in misery
So let's take action
And vow to fight
For everybody's Human Rights!

Stefan Marseglia (13)

THE KNOW-HOW

When it gets tough
And nobody's there
Give me a call
Cos I'll always care
I've been there once
I'm still there now
It's hard sometimes
Till you've got the know-how
My hair's out here
My hair's out there
I can't go out looking like this
Everyone will stare
Stand tall
Walk straight
Eyes open
Don't hesitate
Deep breath
Stomach in
Shoulders back
I'm gonna win
I won't succumb to those fears inside
I won't be beaten, I'm not gonna hide.
So when it gets tough
And nobody's there
Give me a call
Cos I'll always care
I've been there once
I'm still there now
It's hard sometimes
Till you've got the know-how.

Jocelyn Prah (14)

RECYCLING WASTE

Mountains of waste
Mountains of paper
Use it again
Save a tree

Cart loads of glass
Broken on pavements
Will puncture a tyre
Or a child's knee

When your gladrags
Become sad rags
Recycle
As dusters
    collage
    patchwork
Or present them to
A grateful drama society

Metal sources are dwindling
So recycle cans -
And it's not so fantastic
For a worm to meet plastic
So pick up your rubbish
Recycle! Please!

Allison Roberta Jane Colbert (13)

OUTSIDE

The tree is green the sky is grey
I'm laying outside
That's where I lay

The sky is dark, the stars are out
The moon is shining
I'm about

The sun is rising once again
I'm sat outside where I once lay
The tree is green, the sky is grey
The sun is setting here today

And ends this poem on this day
The sun is setting here today
The tree is green, the sky is grey
I'm laying outside here this day.

Aaran Nelson (15)

BUZZY BEE

Once there was a bee
Who buzzed in a tree
He scared every fly
And made the ladybirds cry

Every bird knew his name
And squirrels ran when he came
And even the oak
Gave a scream when he spoke

Yes, I must say
That the bee buzzed all day
He buzzed when he talked
And he buzzed when he walked

So, I say this to you
If you hear him buzz too
Get far, far away
Or he'll buzz you all day!

Laura Ashdown (13)

THE HORRORS OF LIFE

Mothers:
Mothers aren't scary,
They like the house clean,
But when your friends come round,
They're an embarrassing machine!

Sisters:
Sisters are scaredy-cats,
Tadle-tales and things.
But most of all, I hate it when,
When they *try* to sing!

Babies:
Babies aren't all *that* bad.
Ha ha! Only joking,
They scream and howl and cry for mum,
When you take them to Woking!

Brothers:
Brothers can be nice *sometimes!*
Especially if they're older.
But it's nice when things go wrong for them,
'Cause then you can say, 'Told ya!'

Fathers:
Fathers aren't the nicest thing,
Even when they're nice.
Mine says I have to eat potatoes every day,
Well *mine* says I have to eat rice!

All these horrors
Can't be *that* bad.
Of course they are,
(Just don't make them mad!)

Ling Ling Pang (13)

FIVE

I skipped through life,
Happy as sunshine.
I was five and the world was mine.
I had two imaginary friends,
Complete with orange car
And magical world,
A castle shaped night-light
And a tall teacher
Who made me laugh.
Although I was accident prone
There was always my auntie;
Taking off plasters with
Vaseline and love
And an old piece of flannel,
My 'cumfie' which
Smelled of security
And felt like a
Hug from my mum.
I raced the toaster
To get dressed,
Loved everyone generously,
Hid in corners,
Built a huge spaceship
Of cardboard boxes
And flew to the moon.
I remember that happiness
Was being five.

Claire Sissons (15)

GROWING UP

Growing up is kinda scary,
It creeps up on you from behind.
Like a contract that you can't take back,
And you're the undersigned.

Whatever you do, it won't stop coming,
Your body changing inside and out.
The growing pains, periods and the moods,
The changes you're being told about.

Mum saying 'You're not my little girl anymore,'
You get a funny feeling in your belly.
Things you didn't have to do before,
Like showering everyday, so you don't get smelly.

Some things about growing up are cool,
You can go out with your best mate.
Have money in your pocket and a little freedom,
And not have to get back 'til late.

All the things you can look forward to,
Like going to parties and driving.
Having a family and a house of your own,
Having such a good job that there's no need for skiving.

When you look back when you're *all grown up*
You'll wonder what the fuss was about.
Your teenage years haven't been that bad,
You don't really need to shout.

Heidi Warner (13)

ALL THAT HAS HAPPENED I STILL LOVE YOU

When I needed you, you weren't there
When I needed someone to love, you weren't there
When I needed someone to kiss, you weren't there
But I still love you.

I swore to myself I would never fall in love again
Then I met you
Then somehow
It all happened again.

Somebody broke my heart in two
I never thought I would love again
Then you showed me how
But for some reason, you always seemed to let me down.

Jade Okanlawon (14)

NEVER TO BE FOUND!

Dreams are a place of hope,
Water is a place of peace.
Time is placed on everything,
But no one understands.
My world is a place of questions,
It has no windows, only doors.
No one has ever met my world,
Cos it's locked with a single key,
And that key will never be found,
Not even when I die.

Chloe Palmer (13)

THE BEACH

I walk along the soft sand in the hot sun.
The children playing with smiles on their faces,
playing in the sea or making sandcastles.
I can't imagine being young again,
holding your mum's hand when you go down the steps.
She's there to wipe your mouth after you've had an ice cream.

I can hear babies crying and the adults sunbathing.
I stay all day, just watching the sea swishing and swaying,
how peaceful it looks.
I touch the sand and it feels so soft.
All the seashells look colourful
and the starfish glistening at the edge of the sea.
The sun sets and it looks
so beautiful, oranges and reds set across the sky, and the dolphins
jumping above the sea. It would make a good picture.
A man painting
it exactly like it is now. I would call it The Beach.
The beach which
looks beautiful, night and day.
The seashells as colourful as the rainbow.
The children laughing into the night.
                              The beach.

Kayleigh Manciocchi (14)